FIELD EF

ALSO BY THE SAME AUTHOR

50 (F.E.T.)
FIELD EFFECT TRANSISTOR
PROJECTS

by

F. G. RAYER, T.Eng.(CEI), Assoc.IERE

BABANI PRESS
The Publishing Division of
Babani Trading and Finance Co. Ltd.
The Grampians
Shepherds Bush Road
London W6 7NF
England

© 1977 BABANI PRESS

I.S.B.N. 0 85934 042 2

First Published — August 1977

Printed and Manufactured in Great Britain by
C. Nicholls & Co. Ltd.

CONTENTS

TUNERS RECEIVERS AND AUDIO

MISCELLANEOUS CIRCUITS

INTRODUCTION

Field effect transistors find application in a wide variety of
circuits. The projects described here include radio frequency
amplifiers and converters, test equipment and receiver aids,
tuners, receivers, mixers and tone controls, as well as various
miscellaneous devices which are useful in the home.

It will be found that in general the actual FET used is not
critical, and many suitable types will perform satisfactorily.
The FET is a low noise, high gain device with many uses,
and the dual gate FET is of particular utility for mixer and
other applications.

This book should be found to contain something of particular
interest for every class of enthusiast — short wave listener,
radio amateur, experimenter, or audio devotee.

FET Operation

Figure 1 will help clarify the working of the field effect transistor. "A" represents the essential elements of the device, which
has Source lead S, Gate lead G, and Drain connection D. The
path for current is from Source to Drain through the semi-
conductor material, this path being termed the channel. With
the N-channel FET, the carriers are electrons. The Source is
connected to negative of the supply, and Drain to positive.

P-type gates are formed on the N-type channel, providing PN
junctions. When these junctions receive reverse bias, areas
surrounding them are emptied of electron carriers. These
"depletion areas" reduce the width of the carrier channel,
as at B. As a result there is a drop in the passage of current
carriers from Source to Drain. Increasing the bias causes the
depleted regions to extend, and the channel grows smaller,
reducing current even further. Eventually the gate can be

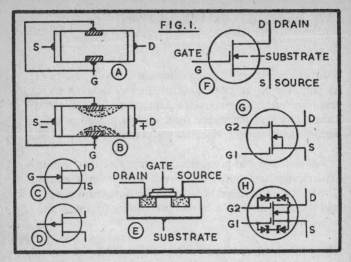

FIG. 1.

made so negative that the channel is virtually closed. This is the pinch off region, and current is practically zero. The current from source to drain, and through external circuit items, can therefore be controlled by adjusting the gate voltage. Since the gate to channel junction area is reverse biassed gate current is extremely small, and thus the gate input impedance is very high. Generally, the gate current is negligible.

"C" is the symbol for this FET, with S indicating Source (negative), G for Gate, and D for Drain (positive). Such N-channel FETs are conveniently operated with a negative ground or source line. "D" is the symbol for a P-channel FET. Typical types and lead outs are shown later.

"E" represents an insulated gate FET. The gate is insulated from the channel by an extremely thin dielectric so that there is no junction in the way described for "A". The substrate is P-type material with positive hole carriers. When the gate is made negative, positive charges move from the substrate towards the gate, so that the width of the conducting channel is reduced, and thus also the current from drain to source.

8

The gate input impedance is extremely high, as the gate is insulated, and may in fact be many hundreds of megohms. This type of FET is thus very useful where a high input impedance is wanted.

"F" is the symbol for an insulated gate FET. The insulated gate FET is readily available with two gates, as at "G". Signal input is to Gate 1, and Gate 2 may be used to control gain, or for the oscillator input when employing the transistor as a mixer.

The extremely high gate impedance of the transistor renders it somewhat liable to damage, and for this reason protected-gate types are popular. As shown at "H" diodes are provided from the gates to the substrate and source, which are normally joined at "G". These diodes conduct if more than a few volts potential should arise between gate and source circuits, and this prevents destruction of the gate insulation, which would make the device useless. Generally the protective diodes shown at "H" are omitted from the symbol of a protected insulated gate FET.

Using FETs

Soldering precautions which are employed with the bipolar junction transistor will also avoid damage to the FET from heating. The essential is to avoid lengthy cooking of the joint near to the transistor. If the iron has obtained its correct heat, and surfaces to be soldered are clean, it is generally necessary only to apply the iron and solder for two or three seconds, and in these circumstances no heat sink clips or similar precautions are necessary. Remove the iron as soon as the joint is properly formed.

It will often prove helpful to identify leads by colour coding, especially when using FETs with different lead positions. With the usual N-channel FET "C" (Figure 1) it is convenient to place a short piece of black sleeving on the source lead, with red on the drain. These indications will then also agree with circuit polarity. The gate can be left bare. With devices having two gates, green can be used for Gate 1, and blue for Gate 2, or as wished. Such coding will also greatly simplify checking connections when the FET has been wired into position.

Particular care is required with the insulated gate FET "G" which has no protection. Because of the extremely high gate impedance, this FET can be damaged by static charges which would be of no importance at all when handling junction devices. Touching the gate leads with the fingers, or a plastic tool, or any metal object, may destroy the insulation. Such FETs are supplied with a shorting collar — generally a small spring which passes round the leads, joining them electrically. This is not removed until the FET has been soldered into position. In most applications, an inductor, or resistor of up to a few hundred k will be present from G1 to negative line, with a lower value resistor from negative to source, and a gain control or resistor network to G2. Once these components have been connected, an external path is formed from G1 and G2 to source, and this protects the FET against static charges. The shorting ring can thus be removed. It must be replaced, or the leads bound with bright, thin wire, if it is necessary to un-solder any item which would interrupt the protecting G1-G2-Source circuit.

This particular precaution is not required with protected gate FETs "H". However, the unprotected type is quite often used, and will be satisfactory when handled correctly.

FET Types

Many FETs are interchangeable in the circuits given here, but it is necessary to check that essential characteristics are suitable. General purpose and audio devices intended only for lower frequencies cannot be used in VHF circuits. All are low power devices, and for a maximum supply voltage of 20v to 30v. It is impracticable to list all types, but those in the table will easily fill the circuit needs of the projects described.

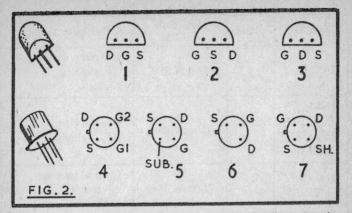

FIG. 2.

Figure 2 shows the leads of the types most generally required. Viewing the small plastic type from below, "1" has Drain, Gate and Source leads in this order, while "2" has Gate, Source and Drain leads as shown, and so on. "4" is a metal cased dual gate FET, while "5" has a separate substrate lead, and "7" a separate shield Sh. "6" has source, gate and drain leads.

The reference number following each FET shows that it has leads identified from the positions as in Figure 2.

FET Testing

Tests which will show whether or not a field effect transistor is in working condition are readily made with a circuit which can be hooked up in a few minutes and operated from a 9v battery. This can be useful when dealing with surplus or other FETs of doubtful origin, or as a test for the FET in a circuit which does not function. It can usually be assumed that a new FET, purchased from a reliable source, will be in working order.

Two meters are required to show the relationship between gate voltage and drain current with the minimum difficulty. Any ordinary voltmeter with a scale of about 0–10v, 0–5v, or less, will be satisfactory, and it need not be an expensive meter with

Type No.	Base	Maximum Ratings	Other Information
2N3819	1	200mW 25v	General purpose AF and RF. N-channel.
2N5457/ MPF103 2N5458/ MPF104	2 2	310mW 25v	General purpose AF. N-channel.
2N5459/ MPF105	2	200mW 25v	General purpose AF and RF. N-channel.
BF244	1	200mW 25v	VHF. N-channel.
7644/ BF244	5	200mW 25v	VHF. N-channel. (Sub. lead omitted)
MPF102	2	200mW 25v	VHF. N-channel.
2N5450/5	3	310mW 25v	General purpose AF. P-channel.
40602/ MEM618	4	330mW 20v	Dual-gate VHF amp. and mixer.
40673	4	330mW 20v	Dual-gate VHF amp. and mixer.
2N3823	5	300mW 30v	VHF amp./mixer. N-channel.
2N2497/ 500	6	500mW —	Low noise. P-channel.
80111	7	100mW 20v	RF amp. N-channel.

high resistance. A milliammeter reading about 0—10mA is also necessary. Single range meters, or multi-range testmeters on suitable ranges, can be used. In Figure 3, M1 is the voltmeter, and M2 the meter to show drain current. The potentiometers VR1 and VR2 are in no way critical, but can best be about

500 ohm or 1k linear components. VR2 ought not to be over 1k; as source current passes through part of the element, so there would be a substantial voltage drop here for other than low source-drain current levels.

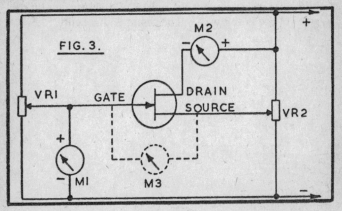

With M1 connected as in Figure 3, and VR2 set so that the source is at 1v above negative, the gate/source potential will be zero when VR1 is also set so that M1 reads 1v. If VR1 is now adjusted so that M1 shows less than 1v, the gate is negative relative to the source, and the current shown by M2 falls. On the other hand, making the gate more positive causes the drain current to rise.

The relationship between gate and source voltages is readily shown by connecting the voltmeter at M3. A centre zero 1—0—1v instrument is ideal here, but an ordinary meter is suitable, with the leads to it reversed when the gate is more negative than the source. A typical general purpose FET gave the following readings:—

Gate/Source Voltage	Drain Current
0.4 negative	1.6mA
0.2 negative	2.2mA
0	3mA
0.2 positive	3.8mA
0.4 positive	5mA

Thus, over this range, a change of 0.8v in gate voltage has caused a change of 3.4mA in drain current.

Exact results will depend on the individual transistor and other circumstances, but the control of drain current by the gate voltage in this way will be absent with a faulty FET.

RF AMPLIFIERS AND CONVERTERS

144MHz Preamplifier

This preamplifier can be used with existing 2 metre equipment, or ahead of the 144MHz converter described later. TR1 is the 40602 or 40673.

Aerial input is to a tapping on L1, and will generally be by co-axial feeder. In some circumstances a short vertical aerial or whip may be used and may provide sufficient signal strength. A high aerial will naturally increase range and many different types of aerial for 2m reception can be obtained. Alternatively, if a start is being made on this band, a simple dipole may be constructed. This can be self-supporting, or of stout wire, and can be about 38½in in length overall, with the feeder descending from the centre. Such an aerial will have little directivity so need not be rotated, and can be raised on a light pole or mast.

For 144–146MHz reception, L1 is permanently tuned to about 145MHz by T1. Input is to gate 1, from a second tapping, and R3 with the by-pass capacitor C2 provide source bias. Gate 2 is operated at a fixed potential derived from the divider R1/R2. Output from TR1 drain is to the tapping on L2, which is tuned by T2. For a narrow range of frequencies such as the 2m Amateur band, variable tuning is not justified, especially as L1 and L2 do not tune sharply L3 couples to the existing 2m equipment — generally a converter working into a lower frequency receiver.

L1 is wound with 18swg or similar stout wire, enamelled or tinned copper. It has five turns and is tapped at one turn from the upper end in Figure 4 for G1, and two turns from the grounded end for the aerial. The winding is 5/16th in in diameter and turns are spaced so that the coil is ½in long. L2 is

15

wound in the same way with five turns, but is ¾in long and has
a centre tap for the drain. L3 consists of a single turn of
insulated wire, wound over the lower end of L2.

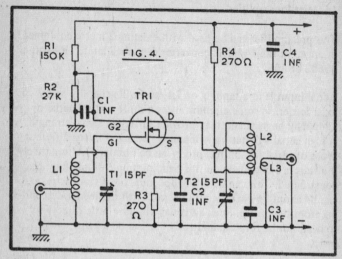

When building VHF units of this and similar type, a layout per-
mitting short radio frequency and by-pass return connections
will be required, and Figure 4B shows a layout for Figure 4.
(Note that TR1 is shown from the top.) A printed circuit can
be prepared to take the components, or plain perforated board
(0.15in matrix) can be used, wired below. It is convenient to
insert pins to take L1 and L2. A small aluminium box will house
the amplifier, and this allows the co-axial aerial and output
sockets to be mounted as shown.

The screen to divide the box into two sections, to separate gate
1 and drain coils, can generally be omitted as the layout does
not allow much feedback from L2 to L1. Tapping Gate 1 and
drain down L1 and L2 also contributes to stability.

A 12v supply is preferred, but this can be 9v if other equipment
provides this voltage and is also to supply the amplifier. The
amplifier can be self-contained if a battery is included in the
box, with on-off switch in series.

16

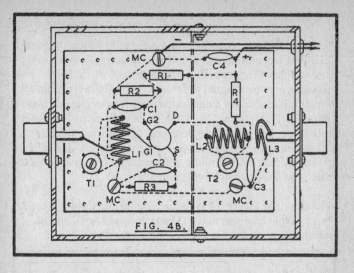

FIG. 4B.

The bolts MC pass through the board and box, so that they can provide a ground return, and they require spacers or lock nuts. (Should it be felt that full details of preparing a printed circuit, or wiring on perforated board, are required, reference can be made to handbooks No. BP30 and No. BP35, Babani Press.)

Should a resonant dipper be available, or be constructed as shown later, this will allow L1 and L2 to be set to about 145MHz. If the coils are made exactly as described, adjustment of T1 and T2 should give resonance in the 2m band. However, slight changes in the length of leads, and similar points which arise in construction, can influence the frequency. So should either trimmer be fully open, stretch the associated coil slightly to separate its turns. On the other hand, if either trimmer is fully closed, compress the coils to bring the turns nearer together. It is possible to experiment with the taps, for best individual results, if the coils are wound with tinned copper wire. Resonance can later be checked when signals are being received through the amplifier. To do this, or tune with no dipper, adjust the trimmers (and coils if necessary as mentioned) for best volume.

FM Booster

For long distance reception, or in areas of low signal strength, VHF FM reception can be improved by using a booster or preamplifier. Circuits such as those shown for 70MHz or 144MHz may be adapted for this purpose. However, a circuit which is intended for a narrow band of frequencies (such as about 70–71MHz, or 144–146MHz) is only suitable when it is to be set up for transmissions near in frequency to each other. For a wide band such as approximately 88–108MHz, efficiency falls off too much at frequencies far removed from that to which the amplifier is tuned.

The circuit in Figure 5 has variable tuning for the drain coil, and to avoid complication the less important aerial circuit, which in any case tunes flatly, is broad banded.

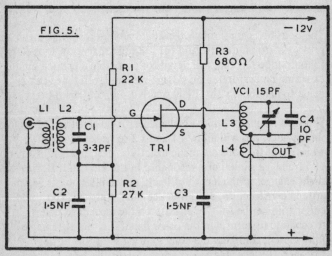

L2 has four turns of 18swg wire on a powdered iron VHF core and is approximately 7mm diameter. L1 is overwound, and has three turns, also 18swg. L3 is air cored, and consists of four turns of 18swg wire, wound on an air cored former 8mm in diameter or 5/16th in, with turns separated by the wire diameter. The drain tapping is three turns from the grounded end of the coil. L4 is one turn, overwound on the grounded end of L3. C4 may be substituted by an air spaced trimmer, to allow more adjustment to coverage.

Values are chosen for a BFW10, which is a low noise, wideband VHF amplifier. Other VHF transistors can be used. A separate battery supply will generally be used, though provision can of course be made to draw power from the existing equipment. The aerial feeder is plugged into the socket connected to L1, and a short feeder from L4 is run to the receiver aerial socket. With a receiver having only a whip aerial, connections will have to be arranged for L4.

When using VHF amplifiers, it will be found that tuning is relatively flat, especially where circuits are heavily loaded, as with the aerial inductor. Despite this, a broad peak giving best reception should be found. It will also be found that the gain provided by such amplifiers is less great than with lower frequency RF amplifiers, and falls off as frequency rises. This is caused by circuit losses, as well as limitations of the transistors themselves. Capacitors should be tubular and disc ceramic, or other types suitable for VHF, and where inductors have solid cores, these must be of VHF type material.

70MHz RF Stage

This is primarily intended for 4m amateur band use, and has a grounded gate FET, Figure 6. A grounded gate stage of this type is particularly stable, and no isolation other than that provided by a layout similar to Figure 4B is required, to avoid oscillation. The gain obtained is less than with a grounded source stage. The tuning of L2 is particularly flat.

R1, with the by-pass capacitor C1, is for source bias, and must be tapped down L2 as the input impedance of TR1 is low with this circuit. It is possible to obtain a slight improvement in

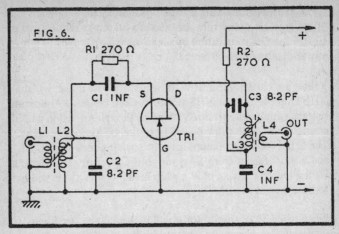

FIG. 6.

results by tapping the drain down L3. The supply can be 9v to 12v, and can generally be from the equipment with which the stage is used.

L2 and L3 could be tuned by trimmers, and be air cored. However, solid cores suitable for 70MHz are easily obtained, so C2 and C3 may be fixed, resonance being obtained by adjustment to the cores then employed with L2 and L3.

L2 and L3 each have ten turns, of 26swg enamelled wire, side by side on 3/16th in diameter (or 4mm to 5mm) cored formers. L1 is overwound on the grounded end of L2, or tightly coupled to it, and has three turns. L4 has two turns, similarly coupled.

TR1 is a VHF type transistor with an upper frequency limit of at least 200MHz. The BF244, MPF102, and similar types can be used. For best possible results with individual samples, R1 and the tap on L2 can be modified, but are not critical.

This circuit is readily adapted for 144MHz use. Self-supporting air cored coils, with parallel 10pF trimmers, can then be fitted. L1/L2 can be five turns in all, of 20swg wire, wound to have an outside diameter of 8mm, and with turns spaced so that the coil is 10mm long. A tap for the aerial connection is one-and-a-half turns from the grounded end of L2, and the source tap (C1, R1) is two turns from the grounded end. L3 is similarly wound. The drain lead can now be tapped to L3, three turns from the C4 end of this winding. L4 is a single turn of insulated wire, closely over L3.

As mentioned, the grounded gate stage will not be found to increase signal strength to the extent obtainable with circuits such as Figure 4, but it has the merit of simplicity, or for isolation from the aerial.

Medium Frequency Amplifier

This circuit, Figure 7, is primarily intended for use over the 1.7MHz to 30MHz range, and will be found to provide considerable gain. RF amplifiers of this kind are generally used to improve long distance short wave reception, to increase volume, and to reduce second channel interference on the higher frequencies.

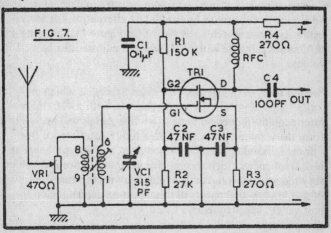

To avoid winding coils and permit easy band changing, Denco (Clacton) miniature plug in coils may be used. These are the "Blue" (Aerial) ranges, valve type. The most useful coils will be Range 3, 1.67–5.3MHz, or 580 to 194 metres; Range 4, 5–15MHz, or 60 to 20 metres; and Range 5, 10.5–31.5MHz, or 28 to 9.5 metres. Exact coverage depends on the setting of the adjustable cores, and will also be modified if VC1 is of different value. The coils are inserted in a B9A type holder. If only a single range is wanted, the coil can be mounted by its threaded end, and leads are then soldered directly to the pins.

VR1 is an adjustable aerial input control, as overloading may easily arise with strong signals. R1 and R2 provide the voltage for gate 2, and R3 is for source bias.

The drain circuit is arranged for capacitor coupling by C4 to the aerial socket of the receiver. This lead should not be unnecessarily long, as this may cause losses, as well as picking up signals which cause second channel interference. If the lead is screened, it must be no longer than necessary. A 2.6mH short wave sectionalised radio frequency choke will be satisfactory for the frequencies mentioned.

Construction is best in a metal case, which can have a hinged lid if plug-in coils are to be fitted. (An alternative, for several bands, is to use switching as shown for Figure 11.) No ganging difficulties can arise with VC1, which is adjusted for best volume.

Second channel interference is caused by signals which are 2xIF frequency from the wanted signals. With a 470kHz intermediate frequency, these offending signals will be 940kHz from the wanted transmission. As a result, interference from this cause is unlikely at low frequencies, but very probable at high frequencies. Such second channel interference is considerably reduced, or completely avoided, by using a tuned RF stage of this kind, actual results in this direction depending on the receiver IF, and frequencies tuned.

A 9v supply is adequate, and current may be drawn from the receiver if convenient. Only about 2mA to 3mA or so will be wanted. The MEM618, 40602, and 40673 will be found satisfactory here.

Top Band Preselector

The 160 metre band carries amateur and other signals, and
Figure 8 is a preselector for approximately 1.8MHz to 2.0MHz.
Here, VC1/2 is a 2-gang capacitor, and thus two additional
tuned circuits are obtained ahead of the receiver. It is necessary
to tap the gate of TR1 down L2, to preserve stability. However,
screened coils are not essential, if L1/L2, and L3/L4 are
situated at opposite sides of the ganged capacitor and arranged
to avoid unnecessary feedback or coupling.

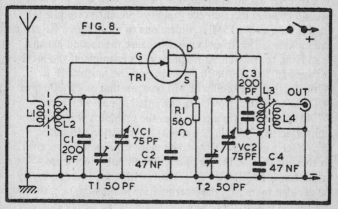

C1 and C3 are best 2% or similar silver mica. All HF and general
purpose FETs suitable for RF use should prove suitable here.
Values are for the 2N5459 but will suit similar devices.

Both coils are wound on cored formers approximately 10mm or
3/8in in diameter, and using 32swg enamelled wire. L2 and L3
each consist of fifty turns, side by side. Begin winding near the
top of the former, securing the wire with "Bostik 1" or similar
adhesive. The whole winding should not be covered with
adhesive, varnish, wax or other substances. L1 is twenty turns,
wound near the bottom of L2. L4 is similarly positioned, but
has fifteen turns. It will couple into the usual dipole or similar
receiver input socket, having a nominal impedance of about 75
to 300 ohms. Touches of adhesive will also hold these turns in
position.

23

A metal cabinet about 6 x 4 x 4 in is suitable for this unit. TR1 and R1/C2 can be wired on a small insulated board, fitted adjacent to VC1/2. C1, C3 and C4 can be soldered directly to the coil tags. Separate trimmers for T1 and T2 are only required if the ganged capacitor does not have trimmers incorporated. Though VC1/2 provides some bandspread a small ball drive or similar reduction drive should be fitted.

13–30MHz Grounded Gate Stage

If a receiver has an intermediate frequency of 455 to 470kHz, second channel interference is always present at frequencies higher than about 15MHz, unless one or more tuned RF stages are included. This trouble arises because the second channel is so close to the wanted frequency. As example, if the receiver is tuned to 20MHz, or 20,000kHz, and the receiver IF is 470kHz, then the oscillator will be operating on 20,000 plus 470 = 20,470kHz. However, unwanted signals which are 470kHz higher in frequency than the oscillator will also be converted to 470kHz. As a result, transmissions around 20,940kHz or 20.94MHz will be passed through the receiver, in this instance, as the aerial circuit will not reject these, when tuned to 20MHz. This effect, with a superhet, can only be avoided by raising the intermediate frequency, or providing additional selectivity before the mixer or frequency changer.

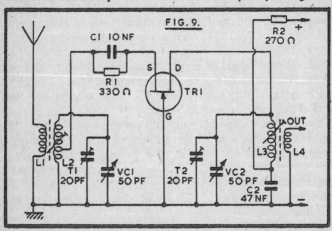

FIG. 9.

The grounded gate stage in Figure 9 introduces two additional tuned circuits before the mixer, so is of considerable aid in reducing interference from second channel signals. By keeping parallel capacitances to a low value, approximately 30MHz to 13MHz can be tuned in a single band, with good efficiency.

L2 and L3 are identical, and are wound with 24swg enamelled wire, using 7mm formers with adjustable cores. The cores must be suitable for use at 30MHz or higher frequencies. L2 and L3 are each eighteen turns, but L2 is tapped at three turns from the grounded end for C1 and R1. Begin winding from near the top ends of the formers, securing the wire with a spot of adhesive. Turns are side by side. L1 is wound immediately below the grounded end of L2, and has seven turns. L4 is wound at the grounded end of L3, and has five turns.

Layout should place L1/L2 at one side of the ganged tuning capacitor VC1/VC2, and L3/L4 at the other side. The output lead from L4 and ground line are connected to the aerial terminal and chassis or earth of the receiver. It may be possible to draw a positive supply from the receiver, 9v to 12v being required here.

No connection must ever be made to the chassis of an AC/DC type receiver which draws current directly from the mains, and may thus have a live chassis.

To obtain maximum band coverage without increasing VC1/2 in value, T1 and T2 must be set at low values. First unscrew T1 and T2 completely. Set the cores of L2 and L3 in approximately similar positions. A signal should then be tuned in around 28—30MHz, and T1 or T2 can then be adjusted for best volume. Subsequently find a stable signal around 14—16MHz, and set the cores for best volume. These adjustments should be repeated a few times, adjusting T1 and T2 at the HF end of the band (VC1/2 nearly fully open) and the coil core towards the LF end of the band (VC1/2 nearly closed).

If the receiver has a signal strength or tuning meter, this will aid critical alignment. Alternatively, choose weak signals or if possible switch off the automatic volume control circuits, so that AVC action does not mask adjustments.

Should a receiver with no RF stage be in use, check that the grounded gate stage is actually being tuned to the correct signal frequency, and not to the second channel, as second channel signals may come through strongly with such a receiver.

With receivers having an IF of 1.6MHz, the second channel will fall at 3.2MHz from wanted transmissions, so is less likely to be troublesome.

11–32MHz MOSFET Stage

This can have similar applications to the circuit in Figure 9, but uses a dual gate FET, Figure 10. Such a stage can provide a very useful degree of gain. It becomes necessary to screen or segregate gate 1 input and drain output tuned circuits.

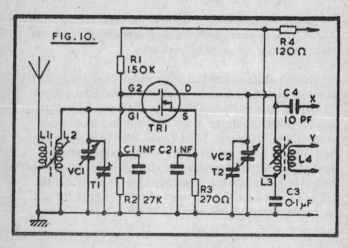

L2 and L3 each have eleven turns of 26swg enamelled wire, side by side on a 7mm cored former. With a 2-gang 100pF capacitor for VC1/VC2, coverage is approximately 11 to 32MHz. Trimmers T1 and T2 can each be 20pF. The coils are wound as described for Figure 9, and alignment of the two tuned circuits is also carried as described there. L1 has five turns, and L4 four turns, situated as explained for Figure 9.

TR1 operates with fixed gain. If a gain or sensitivity control is wanted, this can be added as shown in other circuits. An aerial input potentiometer may be added (Figure 7) or gate 2 voltage can be adjusted by a potentiometer. A gain control is not likely to be necessary when the stage is used before a receiver which has its own RF gain control. Otherwise, overloading of early stages of the receiver may arise with strong signals.

Alternative forms of output coupling are shown. If L4 is used, one end is grounded (see Figure 9) and Y is connected to the aerial input socket of the receiver. This method is preferred where the receiver has the usual medium or low impedance input. Some receiver have a high impedance aerial socket for end-fed and similar aerials which are arranged for high impedance feed, and with these results will be improved by not using L4. Instead, C4 provides capacity coupling to the aerial socket at X. Trimming and alignment of T2 and L3 should be checked after adding this connection and C4.

The 40602 or 40673 will perform well here, though other dual gate FETs can be fitted with satisfactory results.

Segregation of circuits is most easily achieved by using a small metal chassis, with L1/L2 on top, near VC1/2. A lead can then pass down through the chassis from VC1 to G1. TR1 and associated items, including L3/L4, can be under the chassis. This screens L3 from L2. The RF connection from X or Y to the receiver should be short, and away from the aerial lead to L1.

Ham Band Preselector

An amplifier or preselector is often used to improve the reception of amateur signals. By employing a selection of series and parallel capacitors, it is possible to arrange that each band shall completely fill the tuning scale. However, this does not contribute anything in terms of efficiency, and can be tiresome to adjust. For these reasons, tuning here is with the single capacitor VC1, with parallel fixed capacitor C2. Values are chosen to accomodate the largest band, so there is coverage to spare on the smaller bands. This is of little or no disadvantage in practice, since tuning of the preselector is merely to peak up the wanted signals on each band.

The amateur bands are as follows: 1.8–2.0MHz (160 metres), 3.5–3.8MHz (80 metres), 7.0–7.1MHz (40 metres), 14.0–14.35MHz (20 metres), 21.0–21.45MHz (15 metres), 28.0–29.7MHz (10 metres). Outside Great Britain some of these frequencies are extended.

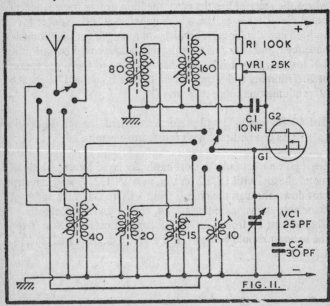

FIG. 11.

In Figure 11, a 2-pole 6-way switch selects the required coils, for 160, 80, 40m and other bands. Signal input is to gate 1. The potentiometer VR1 provides a gain control, to avoid overloading of the receiver with strong signals. Drain and source circuits are arranged as in Figure 7, with capacitor coupling to the receiver. If the drain circuit were also tuned, twelve coils would become necessary, with ganged tuning.

Winding of the six aerial coils is not too critical, as it is only necessary to set the cores so that amateur signals throughout each band can be peaked by VC1. All coils are wound on formers approximately 9/32 in or 7 mm in diameter, and 1 in long.

10m.	Seven turns 26swg side by side. Aerial coupling four turns.
15m.	Nine turns 26swg side by side. Aerial coupling five turns.
20m.	Fifteen turns 32swg side by side. Aerial coupling eight turns.
40m.	Twenty-eight turns 32swg side by side. Aerial coupling fifteen turns.
80m.	Sixty turns 34swg side by side with two cores. Aerial coupling thirty-five turns.
160m.	120 turns in compact pile occupying ¼in width, 34swg. Aerial coupling 60 turns in pile. .

Details of coil winding will be found earlier. It is important that windings are **not** covered with adhesive, cement, or other substances. Winding should begin very near the top of the formers, to give clearance from a metal chassis if inductors are mounted on it. At least one winding diameter should be left between any metal and the coil (say ½in minimum).

Layout should place the switch near VC1 and G1, and should permit very short connections for 10m, 15m and 20m coils in particular.

In view of the number of turns required for 160m, it may be noted that a receiver type medium wave band coil can often be used here. Some coils of this type will reach 160m with the core screwed fairly well out. If not, some turns need to be removed. A Litz wound coil here will give some improvement in efficiency.

Portable Receiver Booster

The range or volume of a domestic portable receiver can be increased considerably by adding an external aerial, and the circuit in Figure 12 does this, and provides a tuned booster stage also. With an external aerial, this can allow a small transistor portable or similar receiver to give good reception of signals which may be virtually inaudible otherwise. The booster is not required for normal or local reception, and it is not permanently connected to the receiver in any way.

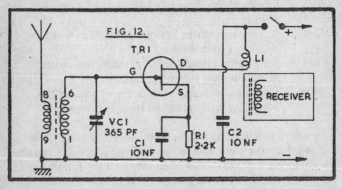

Medium Wave coverage is most useful, and the coil connection numbers are for the Denco (Clacton) "Blue" Range 2 valve type coil. This can be fitted in a 9-pin valveholder, or can be mounted by its threaded end, with leads soldered directly to the pins. Coverage in this circuit is approximately 1.6MHz to 550kHz, but can be varied to suit the receiver by altering the position of the coil core.

TR1, R1, C1 and C2 can be assembled on a small insulated board, fitted near VC1 and the coil. Two thin flexible leads run from TR1 drain and C2 (positive) to the coupling loop L1. This consists of fifteen turns of insulated wire, about 1in in diameter. Wind these turns on a suitable object, slip the winding off, and bind it with cotton to keep the turns together. Connections from the booster to the loop should not be unnecessarily long — about 6in to 9in or so. The loop and its leads may all be one uncut length of thin flexible wire.

If it is convenient to place L1 on the receiver ferrite rod, without in any way disturbing the existing windings there, this provides the closest coupling. Otherwise, position L1 near the rod and its medium wave coil, but outside the receiver. Tune in a weak signal, with VC1 adjusted to peak this up to best volume, and check that L1 is providing effective coupling, as shown by best sensitivity. It is necessary to operate VC1 in conjunction with the receiver tuning, so its scale can be calibrated to agree with the receiver, by tuning in transmissions throughout the band.

L1 and the receiver should not be placed so that there is coupling back to the aerial coil or aerial, or instability may arise. This will cause whistles on all signals.

Best signal pick up will be by an outdoor aerial, and this can be some 20ft to 50ft or so of wire, as high and clear of buildings as possible. However, even a poor or short indoor aerial can be expected to give an increase in volume, especially if an earth connection is also available.

144MHz Converter

The reception of 2 metre signals is generally with a converter and short wave receiver, preferably of communications type. The latter will have sensitivity and selectivity better than average. With such an arrangement of equipment, the 144MHz or other VHF signal is changed in frequency so that the converter output falls within the tuning range of the receiver.

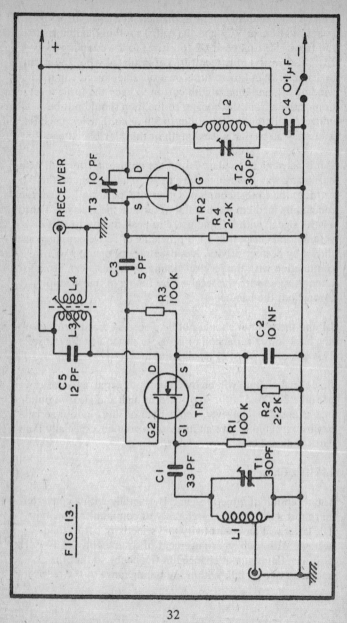

FIG. 13.

32

A converter of this type often has its own RF amplifier, and a relatively low frequency crystal controlled oscillator, followed by frequency multipliers. This allows high sensitivity and excellent frequency stability, but is a relatively complicated and expensive item. Bearing in mind that at this frequency the RF amplifier will not contribute very much gain, and that tunable VHF oscillators are used in many domestic VHF receivers, it is possible to use the much simpler circuit in Figure 13.

L1 is broadly tuned to the wanted frequency band by T1, and signal input is to gate 1 of TR1. TR2 is the local oscillator, and the operating frequency here is determined by L2 and T2. Oscillator injection is via C3 to gate 2 of TR1. The frequency of the output from the drain of the mixer TR1 is the difference between G1 and G2 frequencies. Thus if the signal at G1 is 144MHz, and TR2 is tuned to oscillate at 116MHz, output will be at 144 minus 116MHz, or 28MHz. Similarly, with the oscillator set at 116MHz, an input at 146MHz to G1 will give an output of 30MHz. Therefore 144–146MHz can be covered by tuning the receiver from 28MHz to 30MHz. L3 is broadly tuned to this band, and L4 couples the signal to the short wave receiver.

The oscillator can actually be tuned above or below the aerial circuit frequency of the converter, as it is the difference between converter signal input and oscillator frequencies which determines the converter output frequency. It is also possible to choose other reception and output frequencies, provided L1, L2 and L3 are chosen to suit.

L1 and L2 are wound in the same way, except that L1 is tapped one turn from its grounded end. Each coil has five turns of 18swg wire, self supporting, formed by winding the turns on an object 7mm in diameter. Space turns so that each coil is ½in or about 12mm long.

L3 is fifteen turns of 26swg enamelled wire, side by side on a 7mm former with adjustable core. L4 is four turns, overwound on the earthed (positive line) end of L3.

Layout should allow very short connections in the VHF circuits. A co-axial aerial socket is fitted near L1. A screened co-axial lead is preferred from L4 to the receiver, to avoid unnecessary pick-up of signals in the 28–30MHz range. The converter will operate from a 9v to 12v supply.

L3 should first be peaked at about 29MHz. If a signal generator is available (that described later can be used) couple this to TR1 drain by placing the output lead near the drain circuit. Tune generator and receiver to 29MHz, and adjust the core of L3 for best results. Otherwise, couple an aerial by means of a small capacitor to the drain circuit, and tune in some signal in the 28–30MHz range, to allow adjustment of the core of L3.

It is now necessary to tune L1 to about 145MHz, and L2 to 116MHz, or 174MHz. If an absorption frequency indicator is available, this will permit an approximate setting of T2. A dip oscillator will also allow T1 to be adjusted. (The circuits shown later may be used here.) Subsequently adjust T2 to bring the wanted signals in at the required frequencies on the receiver, and peak these for best volume with T1, and check the setting of L3 core.

The converter is best assembled in a small aluminium box, completely closed, which can be placed behind the receiver. Note that if TR2 is not oscillating, no reception is possible through the converter. TR2 should be a VHF FET, such as the BF244, MPF102, and similar types, and if necessary T3 may be adjusted to secure oscillation here. The 40602, 40673, and similar VHF types will be satisfactory for TR1. If needed, frequencies can be brought within the swing of T1 and T2 by stretching or compressing L1 or L2.

The aerial may be about 38½in long, constructed as a simple self-supporting or wire dipole, with a feeder descending to the converter. Amateur activity is most likely to be greatest at week ends, and in many areas a whip or very short wire aerial will provide local reception.

S.W. Tuning Converter

This converter allows short wave reception with a receiver having a medium wave range which can be tuned to about 1.4MHz to 1.6MHz, or 1400–1600kHz. It has a single range, covering approximately 5 to 15MHz, or 60 to 20 metres, and this includes the most important short wave broadcast bands.

Two transistors are used, Figure 14. TR1 is the mixer, and TR2 the oscillator. Tuning is by the ganged capacitor VC1/2, and output at a fixed frequency in the 1.4–1.6MHz range passes to the receiver from TR1 drain at X.

L1 numbering is for the Denco (Clacton) "Blue" Range 4 aerial coil, L4 being the "White" (1.6MHz IF oscillator) Range 4 coil. Both are valve type coils. C4 is the oscillator padder, and it will be found that 960pF, 970pF or 1000pF may be used, though 960pF is specified by the coil maker. Trimmers T1 and T2 can be integral with the ganged capacitor VC1/2, or may be separate trimmers of about 50pF.

It is convenient to use a layout in which L1 and TR1 are near the front section of the tuning capacitor, VC1. L2 and TR2, with associated items, can then be adjacent to the rear section, VC2.

One of several possible methods can be used to couple the drain of TR1 to the receiver. A radio frequency choke between X and the positive line will allow capacitor coupling, as in Figure 7. It is also feasible to provide a coupling winding on the receiver ferrite rod, as in Figure 12, or use an existing external aerial coupling winding here, in some receivers. A resonant coupling, as in Figure 13, is also practicable, this being arranged for the frequency to be used with the receiver. This should not be too far removed from 1.6MHz or 1600kHz, or alignment difficulties can arise in the converter. If the receiver is of the type which must have an external aerial, it should not be too difficult to find a frequency near the high

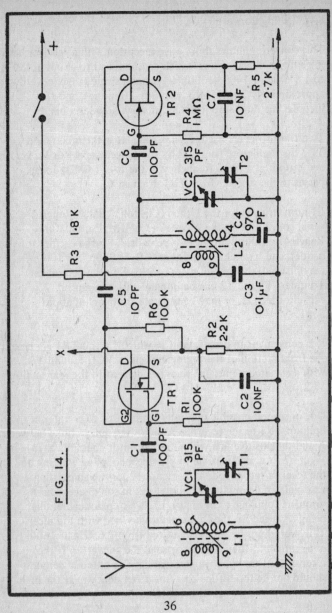

FIG. 14.

frequency end of the MW band where no unwanted signals break through. More care in finding a frequency may be necessary with a portable receiver with ferrite aerial, especially during the hours of darkness.

When a tuning position has been found on the receiver which gives no reception, note this for future use. Switch on the converter and align aerial and oscillator circuits in the usual way.

The low frequency band end reached depends largely on the position of the core of L2, while the high frequency band end depends on T2. Initially set L2 core at about middle position, with T2 about half open. L1 and T1 must then be adjusted for best reception. L1 core is always adjusted near the LF end of the range, and T1 near the HF end. That is, rotate L1 core for maximum volume with VC1/2 nearly closed, and set T1 with VC1/2 nearly fully open.

Should L2 or T2 be altered, to modify the band tuned, then L1 and T1 will have to be readjusted to match.

If wished, T1 may be omitted, and a 50pF panel trimmer can be used instead. This will allow signals to be peaked up critically with any aerial, and eases alignment of aerial and oscillator stages.

With an RF amplifier having two tuned circuits (as example, Figure 10) both coils must tune simultaneously to the same frequency. But in Figure 14 L1 and L2 must maintain a frequency difference throughout the tuning range, this corresponding to the output frequency at X. As example, if the output is to be 1.6MHz, and L1 is tuned to 10MHz, then L2 is tuned to 11.6MHz. As far as possible, this same frequency difference should be maintained for all tuning positions of VC1/2. This is achieved by L2 being of lower inductance than L1, and by the series padder C4.

TEST EQUIPMENT AND RECEIVER AIDS

This section contains a selection of units which will be found of use when aligning or testing receivers and other circuits, or for receiver calibration, frequency checking, or reception of sideband and Morse, as well as checking the output of oscillators or transmitting equipment.

RF Signal Generator

A signal generator is a most useful instrument for aligning and checking the RF and IF sections of a receiver. Figure 15 shows the RF section of a generator, to which modulation can be added as explained later.

L1 and VC1 can be selected from a wide range of values, to secure the coverage required. It is convenient to fit the Denco (Clacton) "Red" oscillator coils, of valve type. With these, pin 8 is taken to drain (S1) and pin 9 to C1. Pin 1 goes to S2 for all coils except Range 1, when pin 7 is used. The appropriate ground pin for each range is as shown below, which indicates the bands

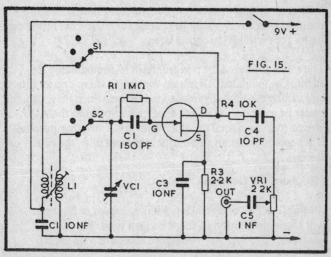

FIG. 15.

39

over which these coils can be used, with a capacitance swing of approximately 20−350pF for VC1.

Range 1.   (5)   380−1600kHz.
Range 2.   (2)   0.8−3.5MHz.
Range 3.   (3)   2−8.5MHz.
Range 4.   (4)   6−22MHz.
Range 5.   (6)   15−45MHz.

If other coils are used, allowance has to be made for the omission of the usual padders and trimmers, as well as for the difference in receiver aerial and oscillator frequencies.

S1/S2 can have as many ways as bands required. However, the higher frequency coils need short connections, and coils must be reasonably separated from each other.

Numerous general purpose and RF type FETs will be found suitable. The presence of oscillation throughout each band can be checked with a meter in one battery lead − current should change if VC1 is shorted. The drain feedback winding must be correctly phased to obtain oscillation.

VR1 is an output attenuator. Construction should be in a metal cabinet, with a reasonably large scale for VC1. Calibration can be by the methods described later.

The signal produced by this generator is unmodulated, or silent. Unmodulated RF is used for tuning sharp crystal filters, and can be used for alignment of receivers which have a tuning meter or indicator, or where a meter is clipped to the AVC circuit to show the effect of adjustments. For other purposes, it is necessary that an audio tone is present with the carrier or RF signal.

Modulated RF Generator

Adding T1, TR2 and associated items, shown in Figure 16, will allow modulation of the RF signal produced by the generator. The first stage in Figure 16 consists of the RF generator, as in Figure 15.

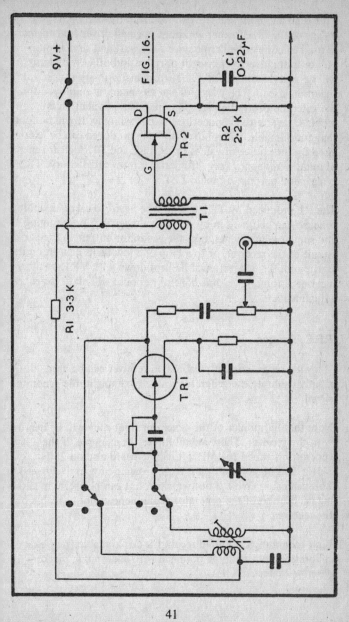

FIG. 16.

TR2 is an audio oscillator, with feedback from drain to gate by means of the transformer windings. A small driver transformer, as used to couple the driver stage to ½-watt and similar push-pull output stages in transistor portable and other receivers, will be found suitable for T1. The original primary is used for the drain circuit. The whole of the secondary is employed for the gate, the centre-tap being ignored. If no oscillation is secured, reverse the connections to one winding. It will be found that considerable control over the tone produced can be exercised by the choice of values for R1, R2 and C1. A clear tone of middle frequency (say 400 hertz) is most satisfactory. TR2 is a general purpose or audio FET.

The RF produced by TR1 will now be heard to carry an audio tone, so can be tuned in by ear with a receiver. For trimming and similar adjustments, take the generator output to the aerial circuit of the receiver, or to a loop of a few turns near or on its ferrite rod. Signal level must be kept down with VR1, or the receiver automatic volume control response will mask exact adjustments.

RF Calibration

If a wide range, correctly calibrated receiver can be used, simply calibrate the generator scales by tuning in the generator signal.

Note that harmonics of the generator frequency will be heard with the receiver. These are multiples. As example, if the generator is tuned to 1MHz, it will be heard also on 2MHz, 3MHz, and higher multiples, these growing progressively weaker. This can cause errors if not watched, but can be useful in allowing calibration of the generator at frequencies not available on the receiver.

If an accurately calibrated receiver is not available, very exact calibration points can be obtained with a harmonic marker, described later.

Signal Tracer

Quick location of an interruption to the audio signal in low level audio circuits is often made with a signal tracer. Figure 17 is a circuit for this purpose. Signals are found with a prod attached to a flexible lead, and coupled to the gate by isolating capacitor C1. This capacitor needs to have ample voltage rating. The clip may be attached to the chassis or ground line of the equipment. Such tests must not however be made with any receiver or amplifier having current derived directly from the mains, or any equipment having a live earth line or live chassis.

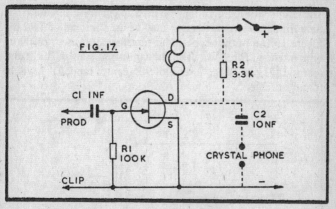

If a magnetic headset of about 500 ohms to 2k or so will be used, connections can be directly to drain and positive, as shown. A 1½v supply can then be adequate. Crystal earpieces or a single crystal unit can be coupled by R2 and C2, and a 9v supply is then preferred.

To test a circuit, the prod is moved point by point from the earliest item where the audio signal is present. This can take in systematically cables, jack sockets and connectors, internal leads and components such as volume controls and coupling capacitors. When the signal ceases to be heard, the fault is known to lie in the last item brought into circuit. Detailed checks here will then show what the fault is.

Any audio or general purpose FET can be fitted. Sensitivity to weak audio signals can be raised by adding source bias — this can be a 2.2k resistor with 47uF parallel capacitor. Overloading or excess volume with powerful signals can be avoided by replacing R1 with a 500k potentiometer, taking the gate to its wiper. The whole unit can conveniently be made in a small box, to hold in the hand, with output socket for headphones or a single earpiece.

Audio Oscillator

The circuit in Figure 18 may be used to generate an audio tone for audio circuit tests, or may be used instead of TR2 in Figure 16. An output type audio transformer is used, of the type intended for ½ watt and similar output stages. The Radiospares T/T7, which has a ratio of 9.2 (centre tapped): 1 will be found suitable.

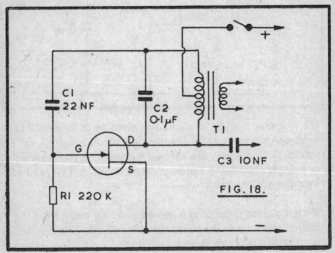

FIG. 18.

Tone and output can be altered by changing any of the component values, or by including a source resistor of 1k to 2.7k or so.

Output, for testing amplifiers or other audio circuits, can be from an isolating capacitor C3 of about 10nF. An attenuated output can be obtained by adding a potentiometer, with output from the wiper via a capacitor.

To test audio circuits with such an oscillator, begin at the output stage or latest point where a signal is produced in the loudspeaker. Work backwards systematically, taking the audio tone to coupling transformer or capacitor, driver stage, and so on. When the tone is no longer heard, the item last introduced into circuit is faulty. This may be a simple component failure; or may depend on associated items, where a whole stage fails to operate. However, relatively few items will need detailed testing.

Any general purpose audio FET is suitable, and a supply of 6v will be adequate. If required, connections to the secondary of T1 can be made, for low impedance tests such as of speakers.

Capacitance Bridge

One of the FET oscillator circuits described is convenient to provide audio for a capacitance bridge. The FET oscillator in Figure 19 can be built as described for Figure 16. The source resistor and capacitor can be chosen so that a strong, fairly high pitched tone is produced. Best values will depend on the FET and transformer, but are not critical. For a 2N3819, a 3.3k resistor is suggested, with 0.5uF capacitor. Rather low frequencies are less suitable, as volume will become insufficient when checking small capacitors.

Audio output is coupled to the bridge by C1. S1 selects C1, C2 or C3 which together with the unknown capacitor Cx forms one side of the bridge, the other side being upper and lower sections of VR1.

Values of 100pF for C1, 10,000pF, 10nF or 0.01uF for C2, and 1uF for C3 will give wide ranges having centre values of 100pF,

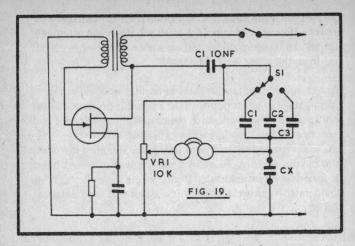

FIG. 19.

10nF and 1uF. VR1 should be a good quality linear potentiometer. Calibration of its scale can be by placing known values at Cx; or the scale shown on page 28 of "Two Transistor Electronic Projects" (Babani Press No. BP30) may be used.

High impedance headphones are most suitable for detecting the audio tone. VR1 is rotated for the null, when the audio signal ceases, and the bridge is then balanced, and the value of Cx can be read off from the scale. When checking capacitors from audio circuits or other equipment, it should be noted that there is often quite a wide latitude in the value, which is not critical. The bridge is not intended for finding the values of very small capacitors, as the audio tone grows too weak, and readings are influenced by stray circuit capacitance. This limits the range for the smallest values to about 10–20pF. The bridge will be found very useful for checking the values of unknown or coded components.

AF Oscillator Prod

This circuit requires no transformer. It may be constructed in a very small space, if miniature low-voltage capacitors and small resistors are fitted. The values shown in Figure 20 will be found suitable, but can be modified to some extent without too much change in the tone produced.

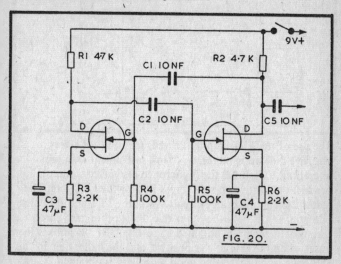

FIG. 20.

General purpose, audio, and similar FETs are suitable. Output is taken via the isolating capacitor C5. This item need only have a high voltage rating if AC mains type equipment will be tested. The safety precaution mentioned earlier must be remembered when dealing with any mains receiver or amplifier.

The use of a prod of this type has already been described. It is employed to inject an audio signal into various points, working backwards from the output stage, until the fault is localised.

The whole oscillator is readily assembled on a small piece of perforated board, with space to accommodate a 9v battery.

Amplified Absorption Wavemeter

A wavemeter is likely to be of use to the amateur who adjusts home built or commercial equipment operating on short wave ranges. The circuit in Figure 21 is for operation over 1.8MHz to 50MHz.

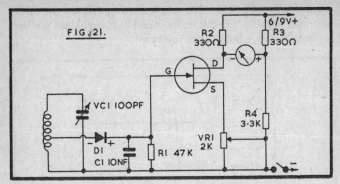

FIG. 21.

The use of the FET amplifier avoids the need for a very
sensitive indicating meter, as a 1mA instrument is suitable. In
operation, VC1 tunes the inductor to resonance so that D1
produces a positive voltage across R1, for the FET gate. The
meter itself is in a bridge circuit, VR1, the FET and R2 being
one side, and R3/R4 the other side. Balance, or zero current
through the meter, is obtained by setting VR1. Balance is then
upset when the gate moves positive, and the indication can be
half scale or more, so that good sensitivity is obtained.

With a 100pF capacitor at VC1, four coils will cover the range
mentioned. These may all be wound on 1 in diameter paxolin
tube, using 24swg enamelled wire. In an instrument of this type,
plug-in coils are favoured. These will require four octal of
similar bases, which may be from old useless valves, with a
holder to suit. With some bases, the two smaller coils can be
wound directly on the base itself, as there is sufficient length
available.

The smallest coil has two turns, tapped at about one turn for
the diode, and its range is approximately 50–20MHz. The next
coil has seven turns, tapped at two turns from the grounded end,
and covers 26–10MHz. The next larger coil needs twenty-two
turns, tapped at seven turns, and tunes 16–5MHz. The largest
coil tunes 5.5–1.8MHz, and has seventy turns, tapped at twenty
turns.

Construction of this type of instrument usually places the coil projecting from one end of a narrow box, with VC1 adjacent on the top, which also carries the meter and VR1. It is then easy to hold the device in one hand, with the coil near the source of RF to be checked, while tuning with the other hand. Four scales can be marked and placed under the control knob fitted to VC1. With no RF present, set VR1 so that the meter reading is just beginning to rise from zero. Any general purpose FET will operate in this circuit.

Aperiodic Field Strength Meter

The device in Figure 22 will operate at any frequency up to 250MHz or even higher if necessary. A short whip, rod, telescopic or other aerial picks up radio frequency energy, and rectification by diode D1 provides a positive voltage for the FET gate, across R1. This FET is only operating as a DC amplifier, and the 2N3819 and other general purpose transistors will be satisfactory.

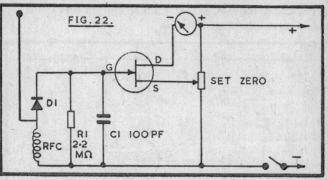

The "Set Zero" potentiometer may be 1k to 10k. With no RF signal present, it allows gate/source potential to be adjusted so that the meter shows only a small current, which rises in accordance with the strength of the RF present. For high sensitivity, a 100uA meter can be fitted. Alternatively, a meter of lower sensitivity, such as 25uA, 500uA or 1mA can be used, and will provide enough indication in most circumstances.

49

Should the field strength meter be wanted for VHF only, a VHF choke can be used, but for general usage over lower frequencies, a short wave choke is necessary. An inductance of about 2.5mH is satisfactory for 1.8MHz and higher frequencies.

The device can be constructed in a small insulated or metal box, with the aerial projecting vertically. In use, it allows tuning up a transmitter final amplifier and aerial circuits, or the adjustment of bias, drive and other factors, to secure maximum radiated output. The effect of adjustments will be shown by the rise or fall of the reading of the field strength meter.

Gate Dipper

Figure 23 shows an extremely simple resonant dip oscillator. It can be used over a wide range of frequencies by the use of plug-in coils. With such instruments, the coil generally projects at one end of the case, so that it can be brought near to the inductors of other tuned circuits.

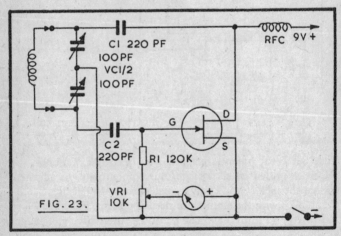

FIG. 23.

VC1/2 is a 2-gang capacitor, 100pF each station. Feedback from the FET drain by C1 results in oscillation, and rectification in the gate circuit produces a small current through R1 and VR1. When a tuned circuit under investigation is inductively coupled to the dipper coil, and both are tuned to the same frequency, RF energy is absorbed. As a result, the current through R1 falls, and this is shown by a dip in the meter reading. Sensitivity is controlled by the setting of VR1. A 50uA meter is most satisfactory, as the dip is small for average degrees of coupling of the dipper to the tuned circuit being checked. However, this is no particular disadvantage, as a clear dip is produced, to show resonance.

Such an instrument is generally used to check the frequencies of oscillator, multiplier and power amplifier coils in transmitting equipment, or the frequency of circuits in converters, HF or VHF receivers, and similar apparatus. These tests can be made with no voltages present on the equipment. To check the frequency of a circuit, the dipper coil is held near the inductor of the circuit, and VC1/2 rotated until the dip is seen, showing resonance. The frequency can then be read from the dipper. To set a circuit on frequency, tune the dipper to this, couple it to the inductor, and set the core or trimmer of the latter until the dip is obtained. Initially, it is usual to have dipper and equipment coils near each other, for ease in finding the dip. The dipper coil is then moved a little away, to loosen coupling, as very tight coupling may upset frequency readings. Coupling is maximum with the inductors in line, near together, but other angles and positions will provide coupling.

The dipper coils can be wound on 1in diameter paxolin tubes, which can have two pins fitted one end, or can be attached to valve bases from old octal or similar valves. A coil for 3—7MHz can have 70 turns of 24swg enamelled wire side by side. For 6—16MHz, the winding can be twenty six turns of 24swg enamelled wire, side by side. For 17—46MHz, nine turns of 18swg enamelled wire, side by side, can be used. For these frequencies, a 2.5mH or similar RF choke is used. The HF and VHF FETs with an upper frequency limit of 100MHz or higher will be found to work well here. The upper frequency limit at which the dipper can be used depends on the RF choke, short leads with low loss construction, and a VHF FET. When oscillation ceases, no meter reading is obtainable.

Drain Dip Oscillator

This instrument, shown in Figure 24, allows similar tests to those obtained with the Gate Dipper, Figure 23. However, the meter M is now incorporated in a bridge circuit, with R2 and the FET on the positive side, and VR1 and R3 on the negative side. In use, VR1 is set so that M indicates about half scale. Resonance between the dipper coil and a coil in equipment being checked then causes a drop in the meter reading.

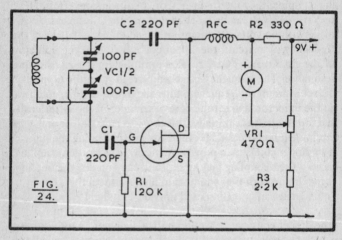

FIG. 24.

Due to the bridge circuit and fact that this is controlled by the drain current, the change present to operate the meter is much larger than in Figure 23, and it will be found that a 1mA instrument can be fitted. With a very sensitive meter, readings can tend to go off the scale too easily, so that frequent adjustment of VR1 is needed.

Uses of this instrument are as described for Figure 23. It is convenient to use a separate on-off switch for the battery circuit, in both dippers, so that the potentiometer can be left set for suitable results.

Crystal Markers

A crystal marker is commonly used by short wave listeners or amateurs to find or check frequency bands, to determine band limits, or to provide exact calibration of a receiver or other equipment. In fact, many of the better communications type receivers have such a marker incorporated.

The marker uses a crystal oscillator of high frequency accuracy, and it produces a range of harmonics, or multiples, of this frequency. As an example of the use of such a marker, assume that it has a 1MHz crystal. This produces a fundamental frequency of 1MHz, and harmonic output at 2MHz, 3MHz, 4MHz, and so on. These multiples can normally be detected up to 30MHz or higher, with a communications receiver of normal sensitivity. By counting these harmonics, at 1MHz intervals, across a waveband, or up or down from any known frequency, a receiver tuning scale can be checked with great accuracy. This also permits exact calibration of a home built signal generator, or similar equipment, by tuning the generator to various marker harmonics, meanwhile calibrating its scales.

The circuit in Figure 25 will be found suitable for crystals through the 1MHz to 7MHz range, using a 2.5mH or similar RF choke. With some crystals and FETs, C1 and R2 can be omitted, though these help easy working of the circuit.

The value of the trimmer is not very significant, but will generally be around 50pF or so for 1MHz, 1.8MHz or 3.5MHz crystals, and unscrewed to 15pF or so for 7MHz crystals. No oscillation may be obtained if the value here is very unsuitable. There is usually no need for a supply of more than 9v.

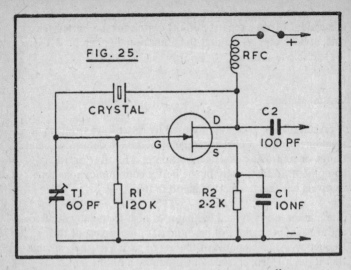

FIG. 25.

Coupling from the marker to the receiver is generally not very critical. For fundamental frequencies or near harmonics, it may be sufficient to place the marker near the receiver aerial lead. But higher harmonics grow progressively weaker, and it is then necessary to place an insulated lead from C2 near the receiver aerial lead, or plug this connection into the receiver aerial socket.

The marker pips are unmodulated RF, so will be found by means of the receiver tuning meter, or by switching on the receiver beat frequency oscillator. (The BFO is a standard adjunct with a communications receiver, but can be fitted to other receivers as shown later.) The use of 1MHz harmonics, for calibration at 1MHz intervals as required, has been described. For amateur band purposes, a 1.75MHz or 3.5MHz crystal may be used. The 3.5MHz crystal would give marker pips at 3.5, 7, 14, 21 and 28MHz, as well as at 10.5MHz (3rd harmonic), 17.5MHz (5th harmonic) and other multiples. The latter are far removed from amateur frequencies, and may be ignored, or used to check receiver calibration generally.

Tunable Marker

The use of a crystal as described for Figure 25 provides high frequency stability and accuracy. However, it is possible to economise by using an LC circuit, instead of the crystal. With such a circuit, frequency accuracy is sufficient for general purposes if it is checked before use, and no crystals need be obtained.

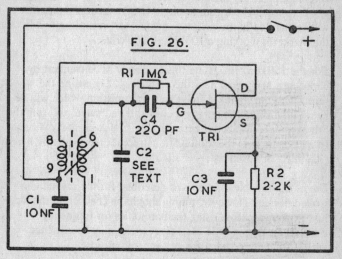

FIG. 26.

In Figure 26, C2 and the associated coil will determine the frequency, which is set by movement of the coil core. Oscillation is obtained by feedback of the drain circuit.

Pin numbers shown are for the Denco (Clacton) "Blue" and "Yellow" valve type coils. Should other coils be tried in this marker, and no oscillation be obtained, reverse connections to the feedback winding. A 2N3819 is used.

Using a Range 1 coil, C2 is 1000pF, for 100kHz. With this coil, changing C2 to 250pF will allow 200kHz to be reached. For 1MHz, the value of C2 is 82pF, with a Range 2 coil.

Coupling to the receiver can be by placing the aerial lead near the coil, or as explained for Figure 25. It may be necessary to remove or reduce coupling from the usual outdoor type aerial, to avoid signal swamping the marker signal.

To tune the marker for 100kHz or 200kHz, tune the receiver to the 200kHz or 1500m BBC transmitter, and adjust the core of the coil until the heterodyne is heard. Set the core for the zero beat position. Rotating the core either way will then cause an audio tone which rises in pitch. If C2 is as explained, this will be the 2nd harmonic, or fundamental, according to whether the marker is working a 100kHz or 200kHz.

For the 1MHz setting, tune this as closely as convenient by choosing a MW signal near this frequency. Then tune the receiver to the standard frequency transmission which will be heard on 5MHz. The core is then slightly adjusted, to bring the 5th harmonic into zero beat with this. Check on the MW band to make sure that the 4th or 6th harmonics are not being heard (1250kHz or 833kHz).

Use of the tunable marker is as described for the crystal controlled devices. However, tuning should be checked in the way just explained before using the harmonics for frequency calibration. With a little care, frequencies may be obtained with sufficient accuracy for any general purpose.

Signal Frequency SSB/CW Resolver

Many general purpose receivers will have frequency bands which cover some of the amateur allocations, but which are not able to resolve single sideband or CW (Morse) signals. With a communications type receiver intended for SSB or CW reception, a beat frequency or carrier oscillator is provided. With its aid, SSB or CW signals can be received. When a general purpose receiver is employed, the BFO or CO can be constructed as a separate unit.

The output of the BFO or CO may be taken to the intermediate frequency circuit of the receiver, as shown later. Alternatively, the beat frequency or carrier oscillator can operate at the frequency of the band being tuned. If so, no actual connection at all is necessary to the receiver, as the wanted signal and oscillator signal are both fed into the receiver aerial circuit.

This method is convenient for the low frequency amateur bands, especially 1.8–2.0MHz and 3.5–3.8MHz. It also has some advantage where the receiver tuning control is of a type which cannot easily provide critical tuning, as the latter will now depend on the signal frequency SSB/CW resolver.

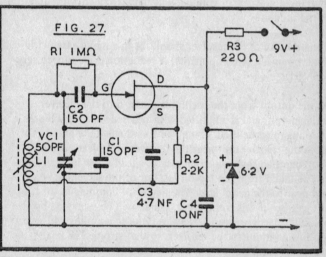

The circuit in Figure 27 will operate at a fundamental frequency of approximately 1.75–2.0MHz, or 3.5–4.0MHz. The former range is suitable for both 160m and 80m, as the second harmonic of the 160m range will provide resolution on the 80m band. However, the 3.5–4.0MHz coverage is more suitable when 80m alone is wanted, or some reception on perhaps 7MHz or 14MHz, with harmonics.

For the lower frequency range, C1 is 250pF and VC1 is 75pF. L1 has fifty-seven turns in all, tapped at twelve turns from the grounded end. The winding is of 32swg enamelled wire, on a 7/16th in or 11mm diameter former, with adjustable core. Turns are side by side.

To cover the higher frequency range, L1 has thirty turns, tapped at 6 turns, with wire and former as described. C1 and VC1 are as shown.

Stabilisation of the oscillator can be omitted when the current is to be drawn from a separate battery, but becomes necessary if the circuit is operated from the same battery as the receiver. Otherwise fluctuations of supply voltage, especially at other than low loudspeaker volume, will cause frequency modulation of the oscillator.

Construction of the resolver should be in a metal case, with rigid mounting of components. A reduction drive is necessary for VC1.

As the output from the oscillator passes into the receiver aerial circuit, and is amplified with other signals, very loose coupling must be used. It may be found adequate merely to place the resolver unit near the receiver aerial lead. If more coupling than this proves necessary, a lead a few inches long can be taken from the tap on L1, out of the screening box, and near to the aerial lead. The degree of coupling is not too critical. But if this is too great, signals will be swamped by the oscillator carrier. Alternatively, very loose coupling will give too low an input to the receiver, so that strong SSB or CW cannot be resolved.

To operate the unit, tune in the wanted SSB or CW signal with the receiver. Final tuning is now done with the resolver control, at the point where the oscillator signal is heard to beat or mix with the transmission tuned in. With CW, tuning is not too critical, as adjustments around the transmission frequency will merely alter the audio pitch. But for good reception of SSB, tuning is quite critical, as the resolver carrier should replace the carrier which was suppressed before transmission as correctly as possible.

Tight coupling of the oscillator is not necessary, and should not be made to an aerial, as this could cause interference to near-by listeners.

1.6MHz Beat Frequency Oscillator

To resolve SSB or CW, a BFO signal may be coupled into the intermediate frequency amplifier. In these circumstances, the BFO has to operate near the intermediate frequency of the receiver, for transmissions of all frequencies. So with a BFO of this type, signals may be received at any frequency throughout the ranges which are provided for the receiver.

Some short wave receivers have an IF of about 1.6MHz. The BFO must then be constructed for this. With most general purpose or ordinary domestic receivers, the IF is near 455–470kHz. If so, the BFO has to be arranged with this in view. Except for this point of providing the correct frequency, both 1.6MHz and 455–470kHz BFO units are the same, and employ the circuit in Figure 28.

455–470kHz Beat Frequency Oscillator

A general purpose RF FET is used as oscillator. Its frequency is determined by VC1, with the associated winding and parallel capacitor. The smaller winding is for drain feedback. A stabilised supply with 6.2v 400mW Zener diode allows the unit to be run from the receiver, if wished.

For frequencies around 1.6MHz, a Denco (Clacton) IFT17 intermediate frequency transformer is used. For frequencies in the 455–470kHz range, the IFT14 is fitted. Each has the parallel capacitor present inside the screening can, in the usual way, and pin connections are shown in Figure 28.

Components may be assembled on a small insulated board, and it may be possible to fit this somewhere inside the receiver. An on/off switch is included in the positive supply

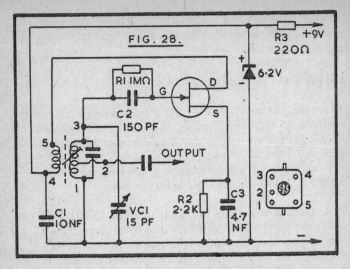

FIG. 28.

lead, as the BFO must not be in use for ordinary AM reception. A control knob is necessary on VC1, as this must be adjustable during reception. If it is not practical to include this control on the receiver, then the BFO can be constructed as a separate unit.

The best degree of coupling from 2 of the BFO coil to the receiver IF circuits needs to be found by trial. It should be sufficient to run an insulated lead from 2, to the vicinity of the first transistor in the IF amplifier. Alternatively, a capacitor of 8.2pF can be included here, as shown, and the output lead can be connected to the receiver diode, at the final IF transformer.

If coupling is too loose, only relatively weak CW or SSB stations will be resolved, and stronger SSB will sound like badly distorted and overmodulated AM. However, very tight coupling is not wanted and will tend to swamp weaker transmissions.

Operation is similar to that described for the signal frequency resolver, except that as all signals are converted to the intermediate frequency in the receiver it is only necessary to make trifling adjustments to VC1. For CW, VC1 will have two positions (above and below the station frequency). But for SSB, there is only one suitable frequency setting for the BFO, as if this is placed the wrong side the SSB signal, speech will be inverted, or unintelligible.

Initially, tune in an AM signal, and set VC1 to about half open position. Then rotate the core of the oscillator coil until a heterodyne is heard, and can be set to zero. Then rotating VC1 either way should cause an audio tone which rises in pitch. Check that this happens with signals on any frequency, to make sure harmonics of the BFO in the aerial circuit are not responsible.

Product Detector for SSB and CW

General purpose receivers have a diode detector, usually fitted for AM reception (and often to supply an automatic volume control voltage for an early IF amplifier). This type of detector can only operate well with CW or SSB when signals are not so strong that they swamp the BFO carrier. The experimenter or constructor may thus wish to provide a product detector, and Figure 29 can be used.

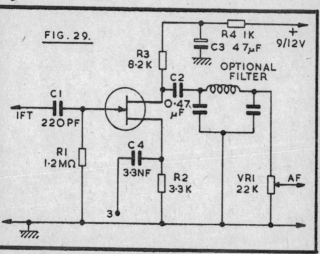

FIG. 29.

Two inputs are required to the FET. That to C1 is taken from the secondary of the final IFT in the receiver. C4 is connected to 3 in Figure 28.

The audio filter is optional, and is designed to reduce the higher frequencies, not necessary for communication purposes. If employed, it can have two 2nF capacitors, with a 100mH choke. The choke, if not screened, should not be located where it may pick up hum from a mains power supply.

After adding this detector, a slight re-adjustment of the tuning of the final IFT may be necessary. The associated BFO or CO is used in the manner already explained.

Where resolution of strong SSB signals fails merely because the transmission is too strong, an easy solution to this difficulty can be found in fitting an aerial attenuator. Figure 7 shows how a potentiometer can be employed, with no changes to receiver circuits.

TUNERS, RECEIVERS AND AUDIO

The FET lends itself well to tuner, receiver and audio circuits of the type which are found useful and popular. Some of the circuits in this section are for use alone, but others will be employed in conjunction with amplifiers or other equipment. Where an audio amplifier is required for radio, disc, microphone or other purposes, ideal circuits and layouts will be found in the "Handbook of IC Audio Preamplifier & Power Amplifier Construction", Babani Press No. BP35.

FET Tuner

A tuner allows radio reception with the aid of any amplifier, so can greatly increase the scope of the latter. In many cases reception of this kind will be of the more local or powerful stations only and a superhet tuner is not then necessary. The circuit in Figure 30 has a single FET as RF stage, followed by a diode detector, and is intended for medium wave reception.

L1 is the aerial coil, and L2 the diode coil, and a matched pair of TRF inductors is required here. Pin numbering is for the Denco (Clacton) valve type coils, "Blue" Range 2 for the aerial position, and "Yellow" Range 2 for the diode stage. VC1/VC2 may be a 2 x 310pF or 2 x 365pF ganged capacitor, with integral trimmers. Separate 50pF trimmers may be added if these are not present.

It is probable that other matched coils, such as those used in a discarded valve receiver, would be found satisfactory here.

Numerous general purpose RF FETs will be found suitable in this circuit. The constructional layout should separate L1 and L2, in the way explained for earlier RF amplifiers. Coupling between L2 and L1 causes the stage to oscillate, so that proper reception is impossible.

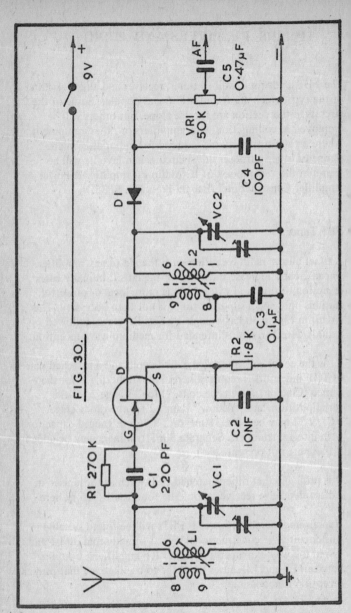

FIG. 30.

64

Where the amplifier has an input volume control which will be used, VR1 can be omitted. Audio output from the tuner is at a much higher level than that from a pick-up or microphone. It may thus be convenient to retain VR1 so that output can easily be set at a suitable level.

Operation is from a separate 9v battery, so that the tuner can be connected to any amplifier without needing to draw power from the latter. It would in many cases be a straightforward matter to arrange that current for the tuner is derived from the amplifier.

Such a tuner will normally be used with a transistor amplifier. It can, of course, operate with valve amplifiers, but it is essential to refer to the earlier notes on safety, in such circumstances.

The aerial may be indoors or outdoors, depending on signal pick-up required, freedom or otherwise from local interference, and similar points. The cores of L1 and L2, and trimmers for VC1 and VC2, are initially set in approximately similar positions. Subsequently adjust the trimmers at a quite high frequency in the band covered, and the coil cores at a quite low frequency, for best results. As these settings interact to some extent, repeat the adjustments a few times.

FET TRF Receiver

Figure 31 is a circuit giving good headphone reception for persons listening, and it can if wished be constructed as a miniature receiver with a short throw-out aerial. Alternatively, it can be used with reduced range by relying on the ferrite rod alone for signal pick-up.

TR1 is the detector, and regeneration is obtained by tapping the source up the tuning coil. The use of regeneration greatly improves selectivity, and also sensitivity to weak signals. The potentiometer VR1 allows manual adjustment of the drain potential of TR1, and so acts as a regeneration control.

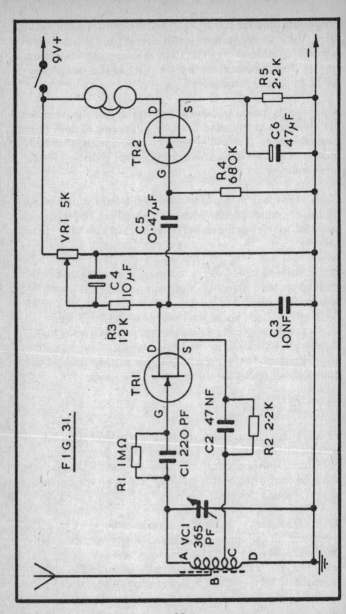

FIG. 31.

66

Audio output from TR1 is coupled to TR2 by C5. This FET is an audio amplifier, operating the headphones. A complete headset is preferable for general listening, and phones of about 500 ohms DC resistance, or about 2k impedance, will give very good results here. If a miniature earpiece is wanted, this should be a medium or high impedance magnetic unit. A crystal earpiece will require resistance capacity coupling, Figure 32.

The tuning inductor is fifty turns of 26swg wire, on a ferrite rod about 5in x 3/8in. If the turns are wound on a thin card sleeve which can be moved on the rod, this will allow adjustment of band coverage. The winding begins at A, and aerial tapping B is at about twenty-five turns. D is the grounded end of the coil. The best position of the tapping C depends somewhat on the actual FET, on the battery voltage, and on whether the receiver is to be used with an external aerial wire or not. Should the tapping C be too near to end D, no regeneration will be obtained, or regeneration will be weak, even with VR1 rotated for maximum voltage. On the other hand, with too many turns between C and D, oscillation will begin with VR1 only slightly advanced, and signals will be weak. Best results are expected when regeneration begins smoothly, with VR1 about half way through its rotation. It was found that only one to two turns were required between C and D. As changing the whole coil by a turn or so has little practical effect on frequency coverage, the best method is to make C two turns from D. Then if necessary unwind half a turn or more at D.

When regeneration is obtained, a heterodyne will be heard if the receiver is tuned through a transmission. VR1 should then be turned back very slightly. Maximum possible sensitivity is achieved when TR1 is almost in the oscillating condition. VR1 has to be set to suit the frequency tuned by VC1, so that final critical adjustment can be made. It is useless to regard VR1 as a gain control, and set it at maximum.

A metal case is suitable where an external aerial wire will be used. Where the ferrite rod only will be employed, for local signals, the box or case must be of plastic or other insulating material.

Amplified Diode Radio

Figure 32 is the circuit of an easily made amplified diode receiver. VC1 may be an ordinary size 500pF or similar air spaced tuning capacitor; or a miniature component if all dimensions are to be kept as small as possible. The tuning coil can have about fifty turns of 26swg to 34swg wire, on a ferrite rod, similar to that described for Figure 31. Or existing medium wave coils may be used. The windings intended for MW transistor portables have a relatively high inductance, and VC1 can then be about 200pF.

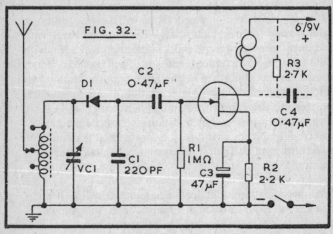

For other than short aerials, it is useful to have tappings, as in Figure 32, to allow sharper tuning. These taps may be at about the middle of the winding, and one-quarter the total number of turns from the earthed end. Some coils may have a primary, or aerial coupling winding, which can be used instead.

Component values are not very critical. The detector diode D1 would normally work into a load of a few hundred thousand ohms, such as could be provided by a 270k resistor across C1, but this will be found of little practical significance here.

The 2N3819 and other audio or general purpose FETs will be suitable. Very good results can be expected from a medium or high impedance headset, as for Figure 31.

With crystal earpieces, which cannot be employed directly in the drain circuit, R3 and C4 may be added. The earpiece is then used between C4 and the negative line. This will also allow resistance-capacitor coupling into an amplifier for loudspeaker reception. A 9v supply is preferred when R3 is present, but this depends also on the volume required.

28MHz Superregen

Superregenerative receivers offer high sensitivity, with a very simple circuit when compared to a superhet. Their main limitations lie in the relatively low selectivity, and the superregenerative hiss produced. However, on some of the HF bands, where a simple receiver is required, such circuits are still practical and can have enough selectivity. The regenerative hiss also ceases, when a carrier or AM signal is tuned in.

A circuit such as that in Figure 33 can be assembled easily in a small box, and has a range of many miles from even a low powered transmitter. It is most suitable for field and intermittent use, where no interference is likely to arise from it.

L1 couples the whip aerial to the tuning inductor L2. It is quite practical to add an RF stage, using one of the circuits shown earlier, to reduce radiation. VC1, with the fixed capacitor C3, allows the whole of the 28MHz band to be covered easily.

TR1 is the superregenerative detector, and a 2N5459 is suggested as allowing smoothest control on these frequencies. However,

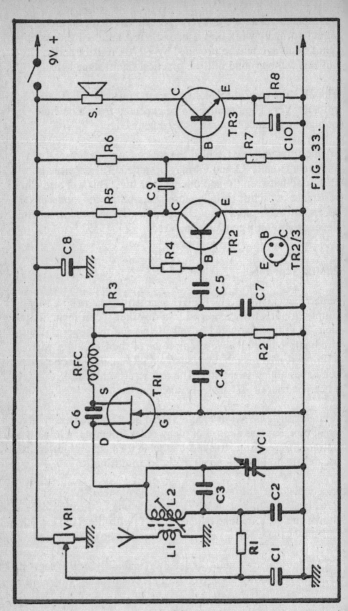

FIG. 33.

Values for Figure 33

R1	1k	C1	22uF 10v
R2	10k	C2	1nF ceramic
R3	12k	C3	22pF ceramic
R4	2.2 megohm	C4	4.7nF ceramic
R5	10k	C5	0.1uF
R6	56k	C6	3.9pF
R7	12k	C7	10nF
R8	39 ohm	C8	220uF 10v
VR1	22k linear pot.	C9	1uF 6v
VC1	5pF variable	C10	47uF
TR1	2N5459	S.	75 ohm speaker
TR2	BC109		
TR3	BC108		

L1, L2, RFC, see text.

various VHF FETs will be found to work reasonably well, though it may be necessary to change the value of C6, or omit this item or fit a pre-set of about 5pF maximum value. VR1 controls regeneration, and quenching is obtained by the correct choice of resistor and capacitor values here.

TR2 is the first audio amplifier, followed by TR3, which will operate a 2½in speaker incorporated in the equipment. A more complete audio amplifier is scarcely justified, though it can of course be used.

L1 and L2 are wound on a 5mm diameter cored former. It is necessary that the core is of material suitable for 30MHz and higher frequencies. L2 has fourteen turns of 32swg enamelled wire, side by side near the top of the former. L1 consists of 6 turns, spaced 1/8in from the grounded end of L2. Too tight aerial coupling may prevent superregeneration.

L1/L2, C3, VC1, TR1 and associated items should be grouped close together, so that short leads are possible. The two AF stages are a little clear of TR1. The RF choke is wound with

42swg wire, on a 7mm or similar insulated rod, sufficient turns being used to form a solenoid 7/8in long. The winding should not be doped or varnished, though small touches of adhesive can be used at the ends, as with L1 and L2.

A telescopic aerial which extends to 20 to 30in or so, fitted to the receiver, will be most convenient for portable use. When VR1 is rotated a quite loud hissing should be heard from the receiver. If this does not arise, L1 may be too near L2, or C6 may be of unsuitable value, or TR1 could be a type not intended for these frequencies. Assuming that the receiver will be used in conjunction with an amateur transmitter operating in the 28MHz band, set the core of L2 so that signals fall at about the centre of the range obtained with VC1. VR1 may be adjusted for best results with weak signals, but its setting is relatively uncritical. No hiss or oscillation will accompany normal reception.

Where an alternative and more powerful amplifier is used, VR1 must be fed from an adequately decoupled supply line.

Infinite Impedance Detector

The use of a 2N5459 or other general purpose RF type FET in the circuit in Figure 34 will be found to give very good results. This circuit provides very little loading for the intermediate frequency transformer. Current drain is very small — typically under ½mA — and a 6v to 12v supply is satisfactory. It should be well smoothed, though C2 and R2 will be helpful in avoiding ripple here.

When this type of detector is fitted in an existing receiver, VR1 will be present, and it is not essential that the value is as in Figure 34. In some home built or other receivers, this may be found to be an easy way of boosting performance. The final IFT will usually need slight re-alignment. In general, there is some latitude in all the component values.

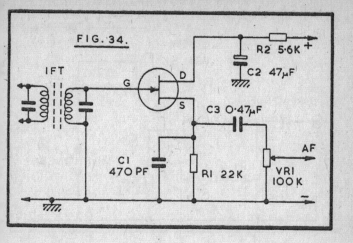

FIG. 34.

Preamplifier for Phones

Figure 35 is the circuit of a single stage preamplifier, incorporating a volume control, and intended for headphones. Component values are for the 2N3819 and similar FETs. Input to the gate is high impedance, so audio may be derived from virtually any source.

The DC resistance of the phones will not influence DC operating conditions (assuming C2 does not pass a significant leakage current). However, much the best results are obtained with high impedance headsets — say 2k, or at least not much under 500 ohm. A very useful degree of amplification is available, allowing weak audio signals to be boosted up to good headphone volume.

It is also possible to connect high resistance magnetic phones between drain and positive, omitting VR1. For other transistor types or a substantially lower supply voltage, it can be worth trying alternative values for R2, to secure maximum gain.

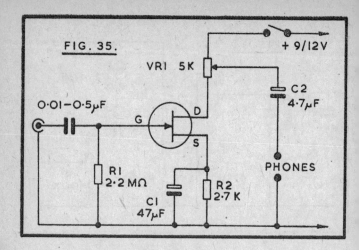

FIG. 35.

VR1 5K

+ 9/12V

0·01-0·5µF

G

D

S

C2
4·7µF

PHONES

R1
2·2 MΩ

C1
47µF

R2
2·7 K

Crystal Microphone Preamplifier

Figure 36 is the circuit of a preamplifier with high impedance input and an output circuit allowing coupling to a main amplifier. It will be found extremely useful for purposes such as boosting the signal from a crystal microphone.

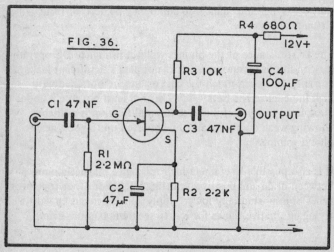

FIG. 36.

R4 680Ω

12V+

R3 10K

C4
100µF

C1 47 NF

G

D

S

C3 47NF

OUTPUT

R1
2·2 MΩ

C2
47µF

R2 2·2 K

The input socket, connected to C1, should take the micro-phone or other input plug, and a screened lead should be prepared to connect output and main amplifier. R4 and C4 provide smoothing and decoupling, so that current can generally be drawn from the main amplifier. It is preferable to use a 2-way power supply cord, not relying on the outer conductor of the audio lead for the negative circuit. A 12v supply is not essential, and the value of R4 may if necessary be altered in value to suit other voltages. The 2N3819 and other audio and general purpose FETs are suitable.

In some circumstances it may be possible to build this stage on a small insulated board which can be included in the main amplifier. This will greatly ease overall assembly. Alternative sockets can allow the preamplifier to be omitted, or included for greater sensitivity, as necessary. It should be clear of AC, power, speaker or similar circuits carrying high current or audio signals, to avoid any difficulties from unwanted feed-back.

Two Channel Audio Mixer

It is often convenient to be able to fade in or out or mix at any wanted level the inputs from two audio sources. The circuit in Figure 37 is suitable for this purpose.

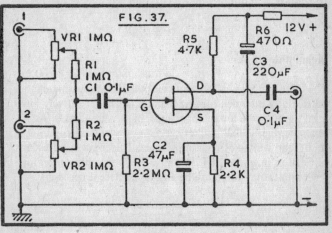

One input is to socket 1, and the second to socket 2. Each input is suitable for high or other impedances, and has its own volume control VR1 and VR2. R1 and R2 are to provide isolation of VR1 and VR2 so that a minimum setting for one potentiometer does not ground the other input. This arrangement is suitable for all general purposes, with microphones, pick-up, tuner, tape, etc.

The 2N3819 and other audio and general purpose FETs will be found suitable. Output is to a screened connector, via C4, and is arranged as for Figure 36. Power supplies may also be provided in the same way as already described.

Such a mixer can be constructed in a small screened box, which is grounded to the negative line. The box will carry the input sockets 1 and 2, with associated volume controls. Running can be from an internal battery supply, if a power connection is not wanted to the main amplifier. An on-off switch will then be necessary in the positive battery lead. There is some latitude in component values, without a very significant change in performance.

Both inputs receive amplification. When one input will be at a relatively high level, as from a radio tuner, it may be preferred to employ a circuit in which extra gain is available for one input only.

Preamplifier-Mixer

The circuit in Figure 38 permits mixing two inputs, and is particularly intended for one high impedance, relatively low-level input, and a lower impedance, higher level input. As example, the "Mike" socket can take a crystal microphone input, and will be of high impedance. This input receives amplification from the FET. The 2N3819 is suitable. Other low-level inputs may of course be employed here if necessary.

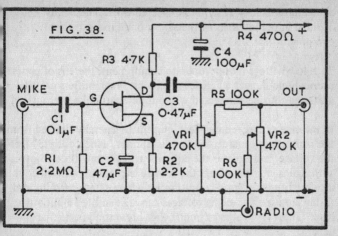

FIG. 38.

The "Radio" socket is suitable for a tuner, or for other medium or lower impedance inputs having a higher signal level. VR1 control the level of the "Mike" input, and VR2 the level of the "Radio" input.

This preamplifier-mixer will be found very useful when employed with a main amplifier where adequate gain is already available for full volume output with a radio or similar input, but which has no mixing facility, and possibly rather low gain for small input levels. Construction, power supply and audio circuits can be arranged as described for Figures 36 and 37. There is quite wide latitude in the supply voltage, but the value of R4 can be modified if necessary, if current is drawn from the main amplifier.

Circuits of this type are excellent for general usage. Where pickup, tape or other equalisation circuits are required, or other considerations arise, reference can be made to Handbook No. BP35, Babani Press.

Safety

The need to observe essential safety precautions has been mentioned from time to time. Otherwise, in some circumstances, shock hazards may arise in unexpected ways. These must be avoided in the interests of the safety of all users of the equipment.

With low voltage battery-operated equipment, there is of course normally no danger whatever of shocks. Preamplifiers or other units can thus be connected without any particular precautions.

In the case of larger amplifiers, current is generally derived from the mains. It is usual to have a transformer, which both reduces the voltage, and isolates the equipment from any direct contact with mains circuits. Where the transformer is of approved double insulated type, in good condition; or where safety earthing and fusing are used, no mains voltages can arise in the amplifier itself. These low voltage circuits thus present no particular hazard.

With thermionic valve equipment, circumstances may be dissimilar. An amplifier may derive HT and heater supplies from a transformer, so that it can have an earthed chassis. This offers maximum safety, though high voltages will be present in anode and other circuits. However, some economically priced amplifiers draw HT and heater current directly from the mains. As a result, a metal chassis, or other items, may be dangerous to touch. It is thus recommended that such apparatus should never be used in conjunction with any circuits in this book, in view of the special isolating and other safety precautions which are essential. Failure to understand or observe such precautions can result in preamplifier cases, microphones, or any other equipment becoming alive at mains voltage, and thus highly dangerous.

Sensitive Level Meter

This circuit incorporates an amplifier, so can be operated from circuits having a signal level similar to about that of a radio tuner or from higher levels. In Figure 39, C1 isolates the circuit from the audio stage monitored. VR1 adjusts the input to the gate of the FET, so acts as a sensitivity control.

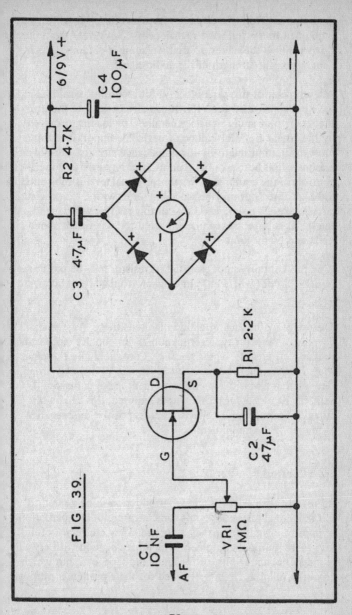

FIG. 39.

6/9V +

C4 100μF

R2 4.7K

C3 4.7μF

R1 2.2K

C2 47μF

C1 10 NF

AF

VR1 1MΩ

D

S

G

Audio power from the drain develops a voltage across R2, and is coupled to the full-wave rectifiers by C3. Current from these flows through the meter, so that a reading is obtained which depends on the strength of the audio signal.

A level meter of this type is useful for recording, a calibrated scale being provided for VR1. It can also be used to monitor the strength of audio signals generally. The loading provided by the circuit C1/VR1 will be of negligible importance for most medium or relatively low impedance circuits. For obvious reasons, AF is best taken at a point after any gain or volume controls in the equipment. Where the signal level is substantially too high, a resistor may be placed in series with C1, at the audio circuit take-off point. The value of this resistor will depend on the signal voltage, but can be expected to lie between about 470k and 10 megohm.

A 6v to 9v supply is not essential. A resistor may be put in the positive circuit, where current is taken from a higher voltage line.

The use of a 50uA meter allows high sensitivity. Any general purpose or detector type germanium point-contact diodes and similar rectifiers will be satisfactory. Care should be exercised when first testing the circuit, by advancing VR1 slowly from zero, so that a sensitive meter movement is not damaged. If damping of the meter movement is required, this can be obtained by connecting a capacitor across positive and negative terminals of the instrument.

Tone Controls

Adjustable tone controls allow reproduction to be altered to suit individual taste, or permit some measure of compensation to improve overall frequency response. They are very useful for general purpose equipment which may be used with crystal or magnetic input units, or for radio and tape, etc., but which do not have input circuits designed for these particular purposes.

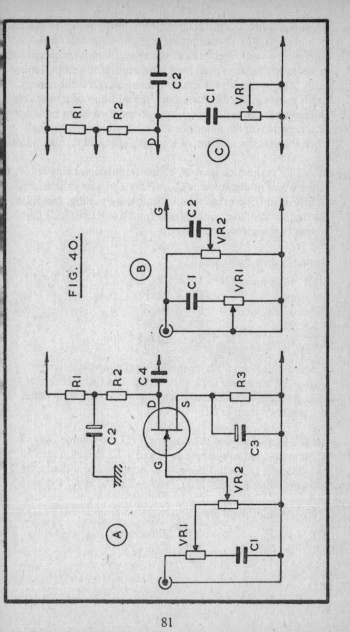

FIG. 40.

81

Three passive tone control circuits are shown in Figure 40. That at A incorporates a preamplifier stage shown in full. With passive tone control circuits of this type, there is an overall loss of audio so that the signal level is reduced. If the amplifier has easily adequate gain, sufficient volume can still be obtained. But if gain is already at maximum, the addition of a tone control network can result in output volume then being insufficient This depends on the amplifier and other circumstances, and when it arises the addition of a preamplifier will restore volume.

In A VR1 is the tone control, higher frequencies being reduced as the wiper moves towards C1. VR2 is a gain or volume control. R3 and C3 provide source bias and by-passing, and R2 is the drain audio load, with output from C4. R1 with C2 decouple the positive supply line.

Typical values for A are:

VR1	500k linear	VR2	500k log.
R1	1k	C1	2.2nF
R2	4.7k	C2	470uF
R3	2.2k	C3	47uF
FET	2N3819	C4	0.47uF

Operation is from a 12v or similar supply, and R1 can be changed if necessary for higher voltages. In this and similar circuits there is considerable latitude in the choice of values for positions such as C1.

At B VR1 is a top cut control, and VR2 the volume control. C2 is connected to the gate at G, and a 2.2 megohm resistor provides the DC path from gate to negative line, other components being R1, R2, R3, C2, C3 and C4 as at A.

Typical values for B are:

C1	10nF	VR1	500k linear
C2	0.47uF	VR2	500k log

Yet another top cut control is shown at C. Here, R1 and R2 are the same as R1 and R2 in A, C2 of A being included as at A. In some cases such a tone control can be added to an existing stage without any disturbance to the circuit board. C1 at C can be 47nF, and VR1 25k. Higher values may be fitted for VR1, but tend to make most of the audible effect of this control occupy only a small part of its rotation. C1 can be increased, to give increased top cut. The results obtained with various component values are influenced by the impedance of the circuit.

With such circuits, low frequencies can be made more prominent by reducing treble with VR1, then increasing gain or volume.

Other circuits are able to offer control of both treble and bass frequencies. A passive circuit of this type is shown in Figure 41.

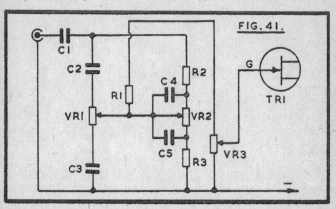

C1 is the input isolating capacitor, and may be unnecessary with some types of input. VR1 is for treble control. Treble is lifted with the wiper towards C2, whose reactance falls as frequency rises. With VR1 wiper towards C3, treble is reduced. VR2 similarly provides lift or cut in bass. Both are linear controls, supplying the volume control VR3 by means of R1. The source and drain circuits for the FET can be as in Figure 40.

Again, values are to some extent a matter of choice, but there is little point in using components which will provide extreme degrees of cut or boost, which will never be required. It is also of advantage to have approximately flat reproduction with VR1 and VR2 central.

Typical values for Figure 41 are:

C1	0.47uF	R1	270k
C2	470pF	R2	390k
C3	1.2nF	R3	18k
C4	2nF	VR1	500k 1in
C5	5nF	VR2	1 megohm 1in
FET	2N3819	VR3	1 megohm log

MISCELLANEOUS CIRCUITS

The miscellaneous devices described in this section will be found of use about the home. It is also economical and convenient to be able to operate most of the circuits described here and earlier from the house AC mains, so a power supply is included.

Circuits Power Supply

Many of the circuits shown earlier can draw current from existing equipment, or can be operated economically from a dry battery. However, in other cases mains running will be of advantage, and this is especially so of circuits in this section which may be left switched on for long periods.

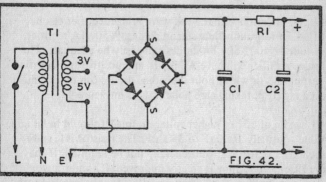

Figure 42 is the circuit of a power supply which can be used for any item requiring approximately 4½v to 12v.

Transformer T1 isolates the low voltage circuit from the mains. A tapped bell transformer is convenient, as this can provide 3v, 5v, or 8v for the rectifiers. Current is drawn from a 3-pin plug which is provided with a 2A or other low rating fuse, and which provides earthing of the low voltage circuit. Should a transformer fault (or other defect) result in mains voltage appearing at the low voltage side, then the protective fuse in the L circuit will fail, so that the apparatus is not dangerous.

Earthing, as provided by conductor E in Figure 42, should only be omitted when an approved double insulated transformer is used.

The electronic circuits described require only a very small current, so that a miniature bell transformer is satisfactory. But should a larger current be wanted, possibly for a signal lamp, the transformer should have a continuous rating of at least ½ ampere.

Taps on the secondary will provide 3v, 5v or 8v. After rectification, the output voltage from the circuit will be roughly 1.4 times the secondary voltage. Outputs will thus be about 4.2v, 7v, or 11.3v.

For rectification, either a full-wave bridge rectifier can be fitted, or four individual silicon diodes. A 50v 1A rectifier, or four 1N4001 50v 1A diodes will easily be adequate. The bridge rectifier will have AC input, and positive and negative output tags or wires. Four individual diodes can be assembled on a tag strip, taking care polarity is as in Figure 42.

C1 can be of 15v or higher voltage rating. It should be of large value -- usually 1000uF to 3500uF. The resistor R1, and second capacitor C2, will generally not be required. If they are fitted, smoothing is greatly improved. R1 and C2 would only usually be present when a positive supply free from ripple is wanted, for a preamplifier, or other circuit requiring pure DC. Quite often components corresponding to R1 and C2 will be present in the supply line at a preamplifier itself.

R1 may also be chosen to reduce the voltage to the C2 circuit, the full voltage being present across C1. As example, assume that power will be drawn from the main amplifier supply, and that the voltage here is greater than required. The value for R1 will then be Volts/Current, where these figures show the voltage to be dropped, and current taken by the preamplifier. As example, assume 12v will be required from a 20v amplifier supply rail, and that 1mA will be taken. Voltage to drop = 20 less 12 = 8v. Then 8/0.001 = 8000, so R1 is 8k. (Note that the same result is obtained by working directly in milliamperes and k-ohms: 8/1 = 8k.)

On the other hand, where the voltage is already not too great, but further smoothing is necessary, then R1 can be from a few hundred ohms up to 1k or so, depending on whether the voltage lost is of any significance.

Typical circuit values for Figure 42 could thus be as follows:

T1   240v/3—5—8v 0.5 ampere
C1   3500uF 15v
R1   470 ohm, or as required
Rectifier, 50v 1A
C2   3500uF 15v
(½w normally easily adequate)

This circuit may be constructed as a separate unit, to be used as a power pack for other equipment. Or it may in some circumstances be incorporated in the equipment itself. Wiring and assembly should avoid any chance of contact with mains connections, switch, or primary connections by the user.

Transformers are available designed for a wide range of current and output voltage ratings, and also multi-ratio or tapped transformers, which allow the selection of any voltage likely to be needed.

Timer

An adjustable timer, giving a delay of about 10 seconds to 1 minute, can be used for photographic and other purposes; or with various games where each competitor must make his move within the agreed period.

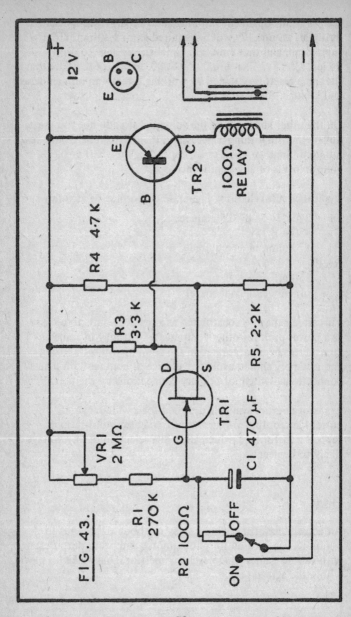

FIG. 43.

88

The circuit in Figure 43 can be employed in various ways, as will be explained. When the switch is moved to the "On" position timing begins, and C1 commences to charge through R1 and VR1. The two resistors R4 and R5 hold the source of TR1 at approximately a fixed potential. When the voltage across C1 has reached a high enough level TR1 gate is positive, so that drain current flows through R3. This causes a voltage drop in R3, so that the base of TR2 moves negative. TR2 is a PNP transistor, so conducts, and collector current flows in the relay coil, closing the relay contacts.

When the switch is returned to the "Off" position, C1 is discharged through R2, so that the interval can be repeated.

A 2N3819 is suggested for TR1, and AC128 for TR2. With C1 as shown (470uF) the interval was found to lie between 10 seconds with a total of 250k in the R1/VR1 position, up to 1 minute with 2 megohm. So the values in Figure 43 can be expected to allow any interval to be set from approximately 10 seconds to 60 seconds. Increasing C1, R1 or VR1 will lengthen the interval. Smaller values here will reduce it. This was with current rising to 40mA, with a 100 ohm relay.

It is not of course essential that these values or transistor types be followed exactly, and other relays would also be practicable, provided the circuit and TR2 allows a satisfactory current and voltage to suit the winding. Generally, a relay with a coil resistance of about 100 to 250 ohms will be most satisfactory.

The relay contacts can be so wired, that when the relay coil is energised, the circuit is completed, or interrupted. The former will most usually be wanted. Closure of the contacts can then light an indicator lamp, or sound a buzzer or bell. The use of opening contacts will be convenient for repeating a set interval when enlarging. A 2-pole 2-way switch is then required, so that switching the timer on lights the lamp to begin the exposure, which continues until the relay contacts open.

For games and similar purposes, a 12 volt 3 watt indicator lamp can be operated from the same 12v supply. Should any kind of mains-voltage circuit be controlled, the relay must be a type intended for this purpose, and care must be taken to arrange mains circuit so that no danger can arise for the user.

'Light' Switch

Switches which are operated by the level of illumination present have quite a number of uses. They can be arranged to trigger by either the presence of light, or its absence. The former will be of use for certain types of warning indicator, slave flash, or garage. The latter method will apply to automatic child's night light, and where a house lamp is to switched on when daylight fails.

The circuit in Figure 44 is arranged to be switched on by the presence of light. The light dependent resistor LDR (ORP12 or equivalent) has a very high resistance in darkness, this falling as illumination increases. When the gate of TR1 is sufficiently positive due to the reduced value of the LDR, source current through R4 results in the resistor R5 and base of TR2 moving positive. The emitter potential of TR2 can be set by VR1, so that current in the relay coil is negligible until the LDR is illuminated. VR1 allows the illumination level at which the relay operates to be set for the purpose required. The relay contacts are connected to the circuit to be controlled.

The 2N3819 and similar general purpose FETs will be suitable for TR1, and TR2 can be the BC108, or similar NPN transistors. A supply line of other than 9v can be used.

'Dark' Switch

It will have been noted that the circuit in Figure 44 could be used to complete a circuit when light fails, if those relay contacts were used which are held open by light falling on the LDR, as described. This would however leave the relay in an

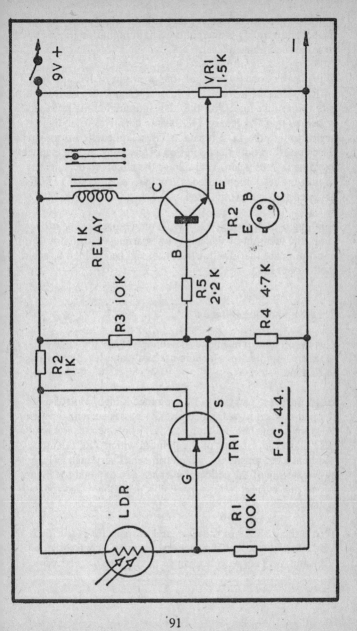

FIG. 44.

energised condition, so it is preferable to modify the circuit, so that the winding is energised when illumination has dropped to some pre-arranged level.

This may be done by changing the positions of R1 and the LDR, so that R1 is from TR1 gate to R2, and the LDR is from gate to negative line. With the LDR illuminated, its resistance is low, so that the gate of TR1 is held negative. When light begins to fail, the LDR resistance rises, and current through R1 can now initiate the operation of the relay, in the manner explained. Once again, VR1 allows the circuit to be adjusted so that the relay is energised when light reaching the LDR has dropped to some chosen level.

If failing light is arranged to switch on a household or other lamp, the location of this needs to be arranged so that it does not illuminate the LDR, or the latter can be shielded to avoid erratic operation.

Sensitive Moisture Detector

The circuit shown in Figure 45 will detect the presence of moisture. Applications include use as a water-level, overflow, or rain indicator.

When the sense pad is dry, its resistance is high. Moisture on the pad reduces its resistance, so TR1 passes current through R3, moving the base of TR2 positive. This operates the relay. VR1 allows adjustment of the point at which TR1 operates, and hence the sensitivity, which can be set very high. VR2 allows setting of the collector current, as explained for Figure 44, so that current in the relay coil is negligible when the pad is dry.

TR1 is the 2N3819 or other general purpose FET, and TR2 a BC108 or other high gain general purpose NPN transistor. VR1 and VR2 allow wide changes in types to be serviceable.

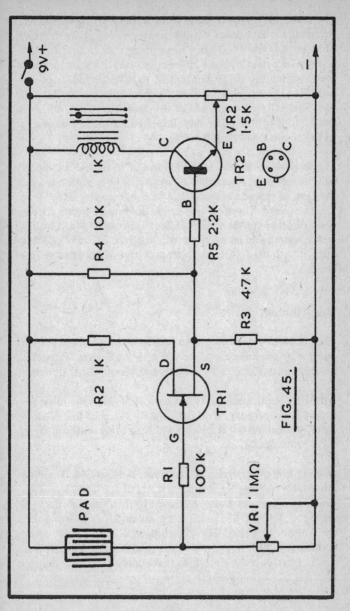

FIG. 45.

93

The sense pad is readily made from 0.1in or 0.15in matrix perforated circuit board having conductive foil along the rows of holes. A board 1 x 3 ins is large enough for an overflow or water level detector, but a larger board (say 3 x 4 ins) is better for a rain indicator. It is convenient to have the foil strips following the longer dimension. Connect together the 1st, 3rd, 5th. . . foils for one side of the circuit, and 2nd, 4th, 6th. . . foils for the other side. Insulated leads can then run to the circuit points in Figure 45.

The warning device can take the form of an indicator lamp, bell, buzzer or audio oscillator, and it can be incorporated in the case, or placed elsewhere and be connected by an extension lead. The sense pad can be suspended over a cistern, pool, or other container to be filled; or it can be positioned where water from an overflow will touch it. For rain indication, place it with the foil strips uppermost, out of doors away from shelter.

Touch Switch

The circuit in Figure 45 can be used as a switch which will operate by touching the sense pad with the fingers. This can be utilised for a child's night light, and various other devices.

With such applications, it is often necessary that the relay should stay energised, until deliberately switched off. Momentarily touching the sense pad will then bring a light into continuous operation.

One method of arranging this is shown in Figure 46. The relay is a double pole model, having two sets of contacts, X and Y. Closure of contacts X allows current to flow through the relay coil, R1, and S1, which is a push switch completing the circuit until depressed. So once contacts X have closed, current continues to flow in the relay coil, until S1 is pressed. Operating S1 interrupts the circuit, so that contacts X open, and so releasing S1 then has no effect.

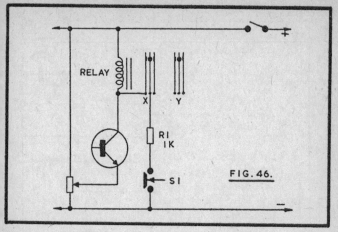

RELAY

X Y

R1
1K

S1

FIG. 46.

The second set of contacts Y controls the lamp (or other) circuit in the usual manner.

R1 and S1 are additions to Figure 45, other items being as shown in Figure 45.

Metal Detector

Many people make a hobby of using an electronic detector to search for buried metal, and some astonishing and valuable items have been found in this way. Apart from treasure seeking, such an instrument can have a more mundane use in locating concealed manhole covers and for similar purposes.

The metal detector shown in Figure 47 is intended to operate in the 95kHz to 105kHz region, and will prove to be an easy device to get working if the search and heterodyne coils are as explained.

L1 is the search coil, and is 6½ins in diameter. This is a useful size, without being unweildly. TR1 is the search coil oscillator. R1 and R2 largely determine operating conditions for the FET, and L1 is tapped so that feedback from drain to gate is obtain-

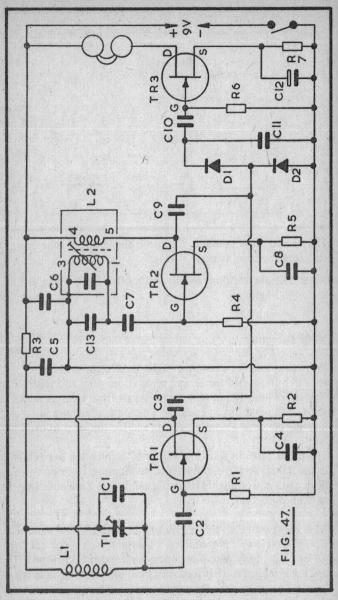

FIG. 47.

Components for Figure 47

C1	4.7nF silver mica	R1	680k
C2	100pF	R2	2.2k
C3	8.2pF	R3	2.2k
C4	4.7nF	R4	1 megohm
C5	47nF	R5	1k
C6	47nF	R6	1 megohm
C7	220pF	R7	2.2k
C8	4.7nF	TR1/2/3	2N3819 etc.
C9	8.2pF	D1/D2	OA91 etc.
C10	0.1uF	L1	see text
C11	1.5nF	L2	IFT14 (Denco)
C12	47uF	Switch	
C13	6.8nF silver mica		

600 ohm phones, box, battery and clips, handle, etc.

ed via C2, in correct phase. The frequency of operation is determined by the inductance of L1, and parallel capacitors T1 and C1. This stage receives current through R3 and has the by-pass capacitor C5.

TR2 is the reference or heterodyne oscillator, L2 is an inter-mediate frequency transformer, with extra parallel capacitance to lower the frequency to 95/105kHz. Feedback to the gate of TR2 is by C7, and oscillation is obtained by correct phasing of the winding 4–5.

Output from TR1 is taken by C3, and from TR2 by C9, to the heterodyne detector formed by D1 and D2. TR3 is an audio amplifier, coupled by C10, and operating headphones. A 9v battery supplies current for the equipment.

When L1 and L2 are working on the same frequency, no audible beat note is produced. The presence of metal near L1 changes the frequency of this oscillator, so that an audio tone is heard in the phones, rising in pitch as the metal approaches L1. In a similar manner, when L1 and L2 are tuned to produce an audio tone, this will change in frequency when metal is near L1.

The search coil L1 consists of thirty-one turns of 32swg enamelled wire, 6½ins in diameter. The tapping is nine turns from the drain end. The coil is pile wound, turns occupying a slot 1/8in wide.

The search coil former can be made from three discs of 1/8in thick hardboard. Two discs are cut about 7ins in diameter, and one which is 6½in in diameter. These are cemented together, with the 6½ins disc between the larger discs, so as to obtain a slot to take the winding. An alternative method, where a lathe is available, is to turn a disc about 7ins in diameter from 3/8in or ½in thick wood, then machine a slot in its circumference 1/8in wide, and to such a depth as to give a winding diameter of 6½ins. In each case the former should be varnished or painted, before winding, to keep out damp.

C1 is 4700pF and T1 is 750pF, so there is reasonable latitude for adjustment of frequency.

L2 is a receiver type IF transformer, as mentioned, and is normally for 455/470kHz. It will be realised that this frequency could be reached by a wide range of inductance and capacitor values, so that the inductance of all 470kHz IFTs is not necessarily the same. With the Denco (Clacton) IFT14, the extra parallel capacitor C13 is 6800pF. Pin connections are numbered for this IFT. Should an alternative component be used, connections to one winding may have to be reversed to obtain oscillation, and the value of C13 may need to be adjusted if tuning cannot be set up as described.

Various FETs were found satisfactory in these oscillators, including the 2N5459, MPF102, 2N3819, and BF244. TR3 can be any general audio or similar transistor, as described for audio amplifier circuits shown earlier.

When constructing an instrument of this kind, it is usually best to have all components except L1 in a case which also carries the battery. This box is mounted near the top of a wooden handle, some 2ft to 3ft long. L1 is fitted to the bottom of the handle, so that it can be swept about near the ground, when walking forwards.

The frequency of L1 can be checked by placing a portable radio receiver, tuned to 200kHz, near L1, and rotating T1. At some setting of T1 a strong heterodyne, or audio note, should arise, and be heard with the 200kHz programme. Slightly detune T1, so as to avoid this, which could possibly cause interference.

The core of L2 should then be rotated, while listening in the phones for the audio tone. There will be a silent position, in which both oscillators are on the same frequency. Moving T1, or the core of L2, very slightly from this setting will produce an audio tone. If this is set at a low frequency, changes to it will be most apparent. If it is found, during searching, that the tone falls, then this can be avoided by setting L2 at the other side of the "silent" position described.

Should further details of the operation of such equipment be wanted, or the addition of a Faraday shield, reference should be made to "How to build your own Metal & Treasure Locators" (Babani Press No. BP32).

Morse Oscillator

Apart from Scout and similar activities, the Morse Code is often studied with a view to obtaining an amateur transmitting licence. Figure 48 shows a simple audio oscillator which does well for this purpose. Output is easily adequate for personal practice with medium or high impedance headphones, or the signal can be fed into an amplifier for use by a group.

T1 is a coupling transformer as used between driver and output pair in amplifiers and receivers. The centre tap which will be present is ignored. The transformer primary is connected between drain and key (positive) and the secondary from gate to negative line. If no oscillation is obtained, reverse connections to one winding. Many surplus transformers can be made to work satisfactorily here.

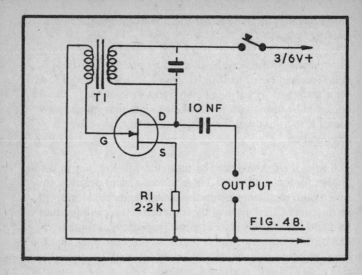

FIG. 48.

The pitch, or tone, produced can be adjusted over wide limits. A strong, moderately high tone is generally preferred. Any audio or general purpose FET should be satisfactory. A capacitor in parallel with one winding of T1 will lower the tone. The value of R1 can also be modified, as can the battery voltage. Loading of the output circuit by the phones will also influence the tone. Little difficulty should be experienced in obtaining a suitable pitch.

When sending Morse, a dash should be equal in length to three dots. The spaces between parts of a letter equal one dot, and a space of three dots is left between letters, and five dots between words. When learning at lower speeds, it is best to form the letters rapidly, but leave longer intervals between them.

The following will prove of aid to those just starting the code:

A	.—	N	—.	1	.————
B	—...	O	———	2	..———
C	—.—.	P	.——.	3	...——
D	—..	Q	——.—	4	....—
E	.	R	.—.	5	.....
F	..—.	S	...	6	—....
G	——.	T	—	7	——...
H	....	U	..—	8	———..
I	..	V	...—	9	————.
J	.———	W	.——	0	—————
K	—.—	X	—..—		
L	.—..	Y	—.——		
M	——	Z	——..		

High Z Voltmeters

A voltmeter having a very high impedance can be made using a field effect transistor amplifier. Figure 49 shows a basic circuit for this purpose, and one which can be readily developed into a more ambitious instrument.

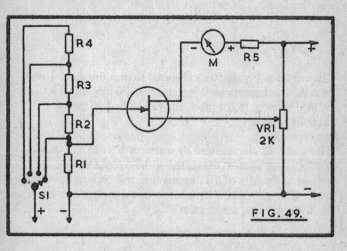

FIG. 49.

With no external voltage present, R1 maintains the gate of the FET at negative, and VR1 is set so that source current through the meter M is negligible. When the gate is made positive, M shows the source current. R5 is merely a limiting resistor, to protect the meter.

Using 1 megohm for R1, and 10 megohm resistors for R2, R3 and R4 ranges from approximately 0.5v to 15v will be obtained. The loading imposed by the instrument on a 15v circuit will be over 30 megohms. S1 selects various ranges.

A 100uA meter is used. R5 can then be 100k. A linear scale is not obtained, but individual calibration is readily made by means of a potentiometer with voltmeter, allowing any wanted voltage to be applied to the test leads. The potentiometer can be 5k, with the calibration meter clipped from wiper to one outer tag.

VR1 in Figure 49 can be of lower value, with suitably chosen fixed resistors at positive and negative ends. This avoids any possibility of severe mis-setting. For a 10v supply a 500 ohm control can be used, with 1.5k to positive and 470 ohm to negative lines.

2 Meg/V 0—10V Meter

The circuit in Figure 50 can be used to measure up to 10v, with an input resistance of greater than 20 megohms. R1 may be incorporated in the prod, and can be two 10 megohm resistors in series.

TR1 and TR2 are balanced by means of VR1 so that no potential appears across the meter, with no input voltage. A voltage at the gate of TR1 upsets this, and current flows in the meter circuit. In use, VR1 is set so that a correct zero is obtained, with no voltage under test.

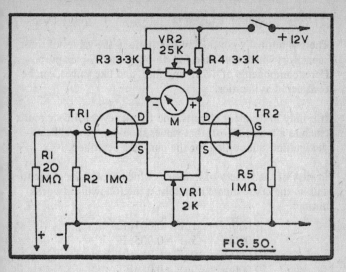

FIG. 50.

The exact deflection obtained with the 100uA meter will depend on R1, R2, R3 and R4, and other factors. With the values given, a deflection of somewhat over 100uA arose, with 10v. Therefore VR2 is provided, and is a variable shunt, reducing the meter sensitivity and allowing setting so that 10v will give a full-scale reading. After setting zero with VR1, VR2 is adjusted so that the current is 100uA, with 10v input. Other readings then closely follow the linear scale. E.g. 10uA is 1v, 20uA is 2v, 30uA is 3v, and so on. It is thus not necessary to provide a separately calibrated scale, for general purposes.

Two 2N3819 FETs can be used. The meter is 1k DC resistance. If R1 is to stay at 20 megohm, substantial changes to sensitivity can be obtained by altering the value of R2. This will allow the instrument to provide the required range, or to permit the use of alternative items in its construction.

A Note on Component Values

There is normally considerable latitude in the values of those capacitors which are fitted for coupling and by-pass purposes. Here, components of 4.7nF and 5nF, and like values, can be considered as identical.

It is only in resonant circuits, and frequency-sensitive circuits (such as a tone control) that values should in general be as shown, unless modified for the purposes described.

In view of the variety of markings which appear for capacitors, and on the components themselves, the following is worth noting:

$$1,000pF = 1nF = 0.001uF$$
$$5,000pF = 5nF = 0.005uF$$
$$10,000pF = 10nF = 0.01uF$$
$$50,000pF = 50nF = 0.05uF$$

Similarly, 47nF = 0.047uF, 100nF = 0.1uF, and so on. The voltage ratings of capacitors will normally be somewhat higher than the actual voltage present.

With any of the circuits given here, 5 per-cent, ¼ watt resistors can be used. Potentiometers for volume or tone control or similar purposes where virtually no current passes from wiper to element may be small carbon types. Where appreciable current passes, wire wound potentiometers are preferred.

Notes

BP30: TWO TRANSISTOR ELECTRONIC PROJECTS
ISBN: 0 85934 033 3   Price: 85p
Approx. Size: 180 x 105 mm   96 Pages
This book is written by Mr F.G. Rayer, a very experienced and
popular author, who has written many books and contributes
regularly to the monthly electronic magazines.   It covers
28 popular projects that can be built using only two transistors. Mr Rayer initially describes in detail the various methods
of construction, Tag Board, Veroboard, or printed circuit and
then carefully details the various projects to be constructed.
An ideal book for beginning and more advanced enthusiast
alike.

**BP32: HOW TO BUILD YOUR OWN METAL AND
TREASURE LOCATORS**
ISBN: 0 85934 035 X   Price: 85p
Approx. Size: 180 x 105 mm   96 Pages
This book contains complete electronic and practical details
on the simple and inexpensive construction of Heterodyne
Metal Locators. This is one of the most fascinating applica-
tions of electronics and an ideal book to capture the interest
of the beginner, also just as applicable to the more
advanced enthusiast.

**BP35: HANDBOOK OF IC AUDIO PREAMPLIFIER AND
POWER AMPLIFIER CONSTRUCTION**
ISBN: 0 85934 038 4   Price: 95p
Approx. Size: 180 x 105 mm   .   112 Pages
This book is divided into three parts: Part I, understanding
audio IC's, Part II, Preamplifiers, Mixers and Tone Controls,
Part III, Power Amplifiers and Supplies. Includes practical
constructional details of pure IC and Hybrid IC and Transistor designs from about 250 mW to 100W output. A "must"
for the library of both beginner and experienced enthusiast
alike.

BP37: 50 PROJECTS USING RELAYS, SCRs and TRIACs
ISBN: 0 85934 040 6   Price: £1.10
Approx. Size: 180 x 105 mm   112 Pages

Relays, silicon controlled rectifiers (SCRs) and bi-directional triodes (TRIACs) have a wide range of application in electronics today. These may extend over the whole field of motor control; dimming and heating control; delayed, timing and light sensitive circuits and include warning devices, various novelties, light modulators, priority indicators, excess voltage breakers, etc.

This book gives tried and practical working circuits which should present the minimum of difficulty for the enthusiast to construct. In most of the circuits there is a wide latitude in component values and types, allowing easy modification of circuits or ready adaption of them to individual needs.

An ideal book for both beginner and advanced enthusiast alike.

Please note overleaf is a list of other titles that are available in our range of Radio and Electronic Books.

These should be available from most good Booksellers, Radio Component Dealers and Mail Order Companies.

However, should you experience difficulty in obtaining any title in your area, then please write directly to the publishers enclosing payment to cover the cost of the book plus adequate postage.

BABANI PRESS & BERNARDS (PUBLISHERS) LTD
THE GRAMPIANS
SHEPHERDS BUSH ROAD
LONDON W6 7NF
ENGLAND

BERNARDS & BABANI PRESS RADIO AND ELECTRONICS BOOKS

BP1	First Book of Transistor Equivalents and Substitutes	40p
BP2	Handbook of Radio, TV and Ind. & Transmitting Tube & Valve Equiv.	60p
BP3	Handbook of Tested Transistor Circuits	40p
BP4	World's Short, Med. & LW FM & TV Broadcasting Stations Listing	60p
BP5	Handbook of Simple Transistor Circuits	35p
BP6	Engineers and Machinists Reference Tables	40p
BP7	Radio and Electronic Colour Codes and Data Chart	15p
BP10	Modern Crystal and Transistor Set Circuits for Beginners	35p
BP11	Practical Transistor Novelty Circuits	40p
BP12	Hi-Fi, P.A., Guitar & Discotheque Amplifier Handbook	75p
BP13	Electronic Novelties for the Motorist	50p
BP14	Second Book of Transistor Equivalents	95p
BP15	Constructors Manual of Electronic Circuits for the Home	50p
BP16	Handbook of Electronic Circuits for the Amateur Photographer	60p
BP17	Radio Receiver Construction Handbook using IC's and Transistors	60p
BP18	Boys and Beginners Book of Practical Radio and Electronics	60p
BP22	79 Electronic Novelty Circuits	75p
BP23	First Book of Practical Electronic Projects	75p
BP24	52 Projects using IC741 (or Equivalents)	75p
BP25	How to Build Your Own Electronic and Quartz Controlled Watches & Clocks	85p
BP26	Radio Antenna Handbook for Long Distance Reception & Transmission	85p
BP27	Giant Chart of Radio Electronic Semiconductor & Logic Symbols	60p
BP28	Resistor Selection Handbook (International Edition)	60p
BP29	Major Solid State Audio Hi-Fi Construction Projects	85p
BP30	Two Transistor Electronic Projects	85p
BP31	Practical Electrical Re-wiring & Repairs	85p
BP32	How to Build Your Own Metal and Treasure Locators	85p
BP33	Electronic Calculator Users Handbook	95p
BP34	Practical Repair & Renovation of Colour TV's	95p
BP35	Handbook of IC Audio Preamplifier & Power Amplifier Construction	95p
BP36	50 Circuits Using Germanium, Silicon and Zener Diodes	75p
BP37	50 Projects Using Relays, SCR's and TRIAC's	1.10p
BP38	Fun & Games with your Electronic Calculator	75p
BP39	50 (FET) Field Effect Transistor Projects	1.25p
100	A Comprehensive Radio Valve Guide – Book 1	40p
121	A Comprehensive Radio Valve Guide – Book 2	40p
126	Boys Book of Crystal Sets	25p
138	How to Make Aerials for TV (Band 1-2-3)	25p
143	A Comprehensive Radio Valve Guide – Book 3	40p
157	A Comprehensive Radio Valve Guide – Book 4	40p
160	Coil Design and Construction Manual	50p
161	Radio TV and Electronics Data Book	60p
178	A Comprehensive Radio Valve Guide – Book 5	40p
183	How to Receive Foreign TV Programmes on your Set by Simple Mods.	35p
196	AF–RF Reactance – Frequency Chart for Constructors	15p
200	Handbook of Practical Electronic Musical Novelties	50p
201	Practical Transistorised Novelties for Hi-Fi Enthusiasts	35p
202	Handbook of Integrated Circuits (IC's) Equivalents and Substitutes	75p
203	IC's and Transistor Gadgets Construction Handbook	60p
204	Second Book of Hi-Fi Loudspeaker Enclosures	60p
205	First Book of Hi-Fi Loudspeaker Enclosures	60p
206	Practical Transistor Circuits for Modern Test Equipment	60p
207	Practical Electronic Science Projects	75p
208	Practical Stereo and Quadrophony Handbook	75p
209	Modern Tape Recording Handbook	75p
210	The Complete Car Radio Manual	75p
211	First Book of Diode Characteristics Equivalents and Substitutes	95p
213	Electronic Circuits for Model Railways	85p
214	Audio Enthusiasts Handbook	85p
215	Shortwave Circuits and Gear for Experimenters and Radio Hams	85p
216	Electronic Gadgets and Games	85p
217	Solid State Power Supply Handbook	85p
218	Build Your Own Electronic Experimenters Laboratory	85p
219	Solid State Novelty Projects	85p
220	Build Your Own Solid State Hi-Fi and Audio Accessories	85p
221	28 Tested Transistor Projects	95p
222	Solid State Short Wave Receivers for Beginners	95p
223	50 Projects using IC CA3130	95p
224	50 CMOS IC Projects	95p
225	A Practical Introduction to Digital IC's	95p
226	How to Build Advanced Short Wave Receivers	1.20p
RCC	Resistor Colour Code Disc Calculator	10p

The Grampians, Shepherds Bush Road, London W6 7NF, England

Telephone: 01–603 2581/7296